reproducible activity handouts created for facilitators

A sampler collection of...

Activities of Daily Living	Parenting
Combatting Stigma	Relationships
Communication	Responsibility
Coping with Serious Mental Illness	Self-Esteem
Home Management	Sexual Health
Humor	Social Skills
Job Readiness	Stress Management
Journalizing	Suicide Issues
Leisure	Values

Kathy L. Korb-Khalsa, OTR/L   Estelle A. Leutenberg

With pride, we dedicate Life Management Skills IV
to the memory of father and grandfather

Meyer Atkin

for his love, kindness, wisdom, unyielding faith . . . and his total acceptance.

Special thanks to the following therapists, counselors and educators, whose submissions of activity handouts for Life Management Skills IV were selected.
The Facilitator's Information Sheet on the back of each handout has a box identifying the submitter(s) and their involvement.

Donald B. Ardell, PhD
Teresa A. Bachtel, COTA/L
Deena Baenen, MA, COTA/L
Sharon Bowen, RPN
Marie Calabrese, RN, MA
Erika Pond Clements, B.Sc., O.T.(c)
Sandra Barker Dunbar, MA, OTR
Natalie Gorlin, OTR
Laura M. Grogan, OTR/L
Diane Hausler, LSW
Elaine M. Hyla, M.Ed.
Pamela A. Joy, COTA/L
Jennifer E. Laabs, CTRS
K. Oscar Larson, OTR, MA
Terri Marshall-Schrader, M.Ed.
Hector L. Merced, OTR/L
Bettie Michelson, MS, OTR
Mary Beth Modic, RN, MSN
Maggie Moriarty, M.Ed., COTA/L
Ann M. Murphy, M.Ed.
John F. Murphy, M.Ed.
Tamara Nance, MA, LPC, RNC
Sandra Negley, MTRS, CTRS
Bonny A. Reed-Bell, OTR/L
Lori Rosenberg, MS, CTRS, RTCR
Corrie Trattner, MS, OTR/L
Michele Vitelli, BA
Dr. Ann E. Weeks

We wish to thank the following family, friends and associates for their support and feedback:

American Red Cross Blood Services
Barberton Citizens Hospital 4N Staff
Jeffrey Brooks, CPA
Scott S. Carpenter, MSCI from Interventions, Co.
CDC National HIV and AIDS hotline
Joyce Engel, PhD, OTR/L
Susan B. Fine, MA, OTR, FAOTA
Claire Frese
Drs. Penelope & Frederick Frese
Deanne Ginns-Gruenberg, MA, LLP, LPC, BSN
Paula Hargrove
Tracie Hruska
Myron Jaffe, Advocate
Kathleen Kannenberg, MA, OTR
David M. Kudla
Susan F. Miller, OTR/L
Robert Charles Neillie
Gary S. Okin, JD
Sondra Sexton-Jones, MS, LPC
Julius Simmons, LISW
Barbara Sledz
Bonnie Spiess, M.Ed.
E. Fuller Torrey, MD
Adina Wrobleski, Suicidologist
Heights Negative/Desktop Service Bureau friends
NARSAD (National Alliance for Research on Schizophrenia and Depression)
Elaine Sullivan, MC, LPC, NCC, Director, Survivor Division, American Assn. of Suicidology

and special thanks to S.D. Khalsa and Jay Leutenberg, husbands and supports extraordinaire!

FOREWORD

The inspiration for our LIFE MANAGEMENT SKILLS books originated from an ongoing practical need observed within a mental health setting. Handouts had been typically used in treatment as a launching pad for activities, an organizational tool, a visual aid, a tangible reminder of information presented, and as a method for building rapport. However, available handouts often did not meet necessary, high-quality standards in content desired, format, appearance and organization – and lacked permission for reproduction.

We have attempted to meet these standards by offering this sampler collection of handouts which are highly reproducible, organized in a logical manner, designed for specific well-defined purposes, and activity-based, allowing for extensive client involvement. The graphic representations are intentionally different from handout to handout in typestyle, art and design to increase visual appeal, provide variety and clarify meaning.

LIFE MANAGEMENT SKILLS handouts are adaptable and have a broad usage enabling therapists, social workers, nurses, teachers, psychologists, counselors and other professionals to focus on specific goals with their specified populations.

The book has been designed to offer reproducible handouts on the front of each page and nonreproducible facilitator's information on the reverse side. The Facilitator's Information Sheet includes the following sections: Purpose, General Comments and Possible Activities.

We specifically chose spiral binding to allow for easier and accurate reproduction, an especially white paper for clear, sharp copies, and a heavier paper stock for its durability and opacity. If adaptations to any of the handouts are desired, it is recommended to make one copy of the handout, include the changes which will meet *your* specific needs, and then use this copy as the original.

We hope that you will find these handouts in LIFE MANAGEMENT SKILLS IV fun, innovative and informative. We wish you much success with your therapeutic and educational endeavors and hope we can continue to be of assistance. Remember . . . creative handouts will hopefully generate creative activities and contribute to a greater sense of WELLNESS!

Wellness Reproductions Inc.

Kathy L. Korb-Khalsa   Estelle A. Leutenberg

THANK YOU TO AMY LEUTENBERG . . .

our Wellness Reproductions artist, whose creativity and skill as an illustrator, and experience with clients, gave the Life Management Skills IV book unique, humorous, and meaningful artwork, and whose insights from her clinical work offered guidance on the content as well. Amy L. Leutenberg, Licensed Social Worker, received her Masters of Science in Social Administration from the Mandel School of Applied Social Sciences, Case Western Reserve University. Her art training was received at Kent State University where she achieved a BFA in Studio Art. She continues to pursue her career as an artist, as well as facilitating wellness with members of the community in crisis.

WELLNESS REPRODUCTIONS INC.

is an innovative company which began in 1988. As developers of creative therapeutic and educational products, we have a strong commitment to the mental health profession. Our rapidly growing business began by authoring and self-publishing the book LIFE MANAGEMENT SKILLS I. We have extended our product line to include group presentation posters, a therapeutic board game, various EMOTIONS© identification products, LIFE MANAGEMENT SKILLS II, III, IV, SEALS + PLUS and SEALS II books and cards, Self-Reflections poster series and educational products about serious mental illness. Our books are created with feedback from our customers. Please refer to the last page of this book, our "FEEDBACK" page, and let us hear from YOU!

23945 Mercantile Road • Beachwood, Ohio 44122-5924
800 / 669-9208 • FAX 216 / 831-1355

TABLE OF CONTENTS

Page numbers are on the Facilitator's Information Sheet, located on the reverse side of each handout.

* *presentation poster available (see order form - last page)*

[over for Supplemental Section]

TABLE OF CONTENTS

* *presentation poster available (see order form - last page)*

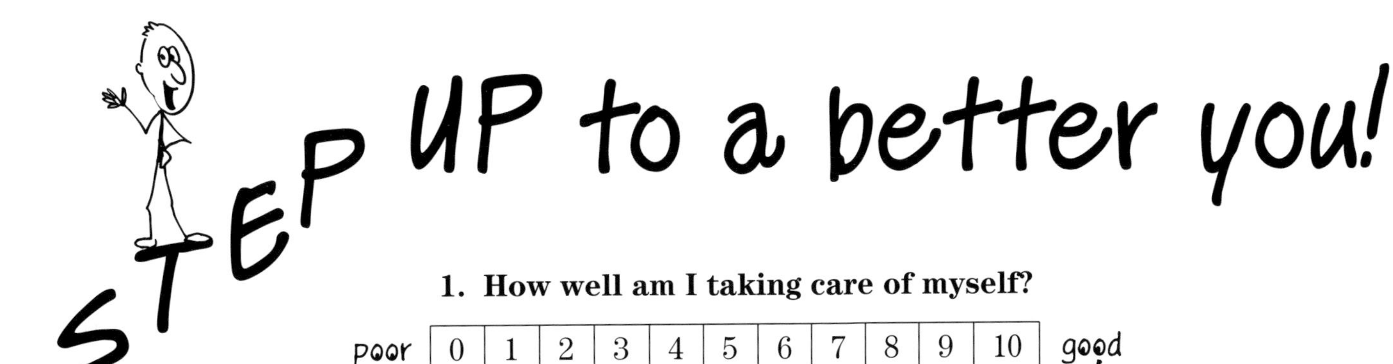

1. How well am I taking care of myself?

poor	0	1	2	3	4	5	6	7	8	9	10	good

2. What influences how well I take care of myself?

____

____

3. What steps do I need to take to improve my self-care?

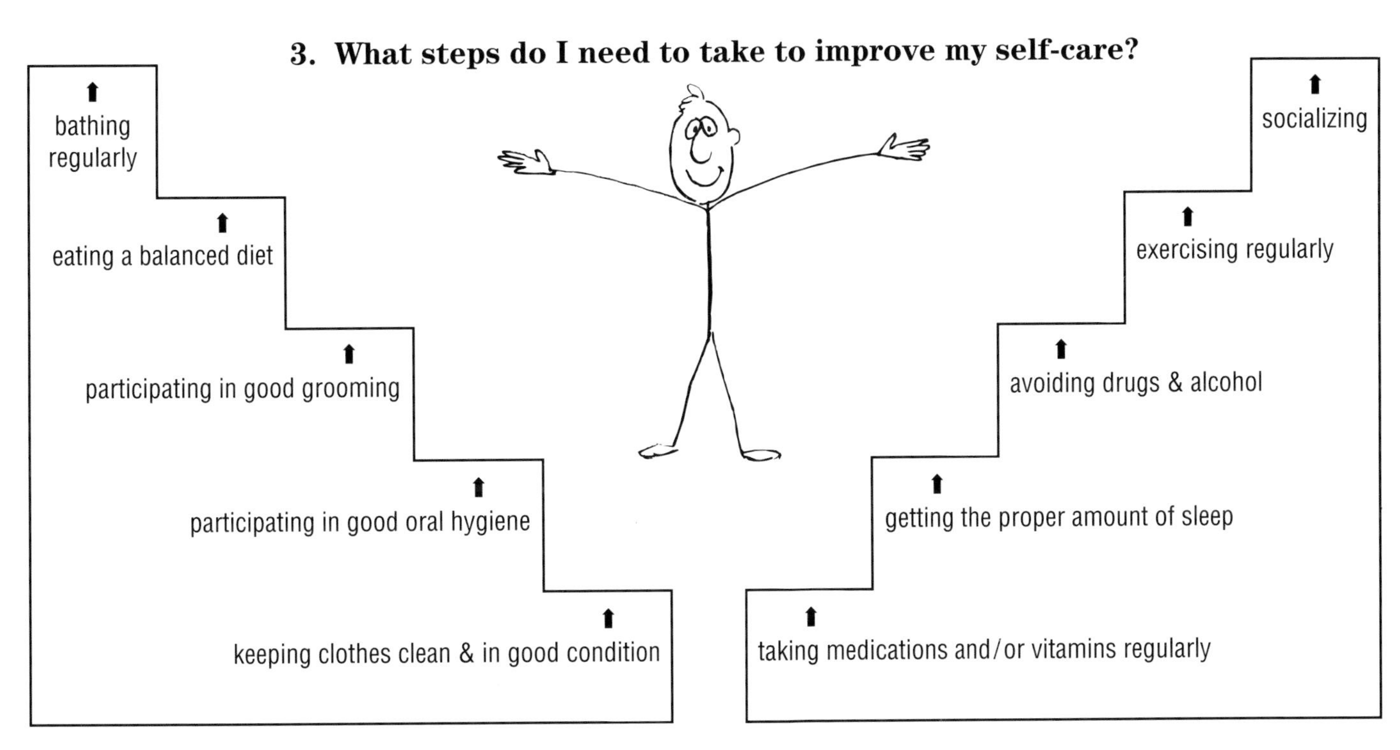

4. Write 2 goals to ensure follow-through with above identified self-care activities.

I will ____

I will ____

5. Who can I share these goals with to achieve success?

____

STEP UP to a better you!

I. PURPOSE:

To increase awareness of an individual's level of self-care and allow for independent goal setting to improve that level.

II. GENERAL COMMENTS:

We all agree that self-care is important, but the level of self-care performed is as individualized as the person themselves. Decreased emotional, mental and physical health may interfere with a person's ability to perform self-care activities. Allowing for a person to choose what is important to them will encourage follow-through and allow for increased self-esteem.

III. POSSIBLE ACTIVITIES:

A. 1. Distribute handouts.
   2. Encourage group members to complete steps #1 and #2.
   3. Discuss as a group what causes a person to stop taking care of themselves and how that affects self-esteem, relationships and general outlook.
   4. Ask the group members to cut out the ten boxes at the bottom of the page and place a box on each step that is a self-care activity needing improvement for step #3. (Use tape or glue to place boxes on steps.)
   5. Finish activity by completing steps #4 and #5.
   6. Process by asking group members to share goals.

B. 1. Distribute handouts.
   2. Encourage group members to complete steps #1 and #2.
   3. Ask group members to share the last time each felt good about themselves, and on a scale of 0 - 10, how each was able to take care of him/herself at that time.
   4. Instruct group members to cut out the ten boxes at the bottom of the page and place them on the steps that they feel will lead them back in the direction of feeling as good about themselves as initially shared with the group for step #3.
   5. Using a chalkboard or dry erase board encourage group members to brainstorm possible goals for improving self-care and then choose two to complete step #4.
   6. Discuss benefits of sharing goals with a significant person to achieve those goals.
   7. Process the benefits of this activity and encourage group members to place this handout in a conspicuous spot (bathroom, refrigerator, bedroom mirror, etc.) as a visual reminder.

Activity handout and facilitator's information adapted from submission by Teresa A. Bachtel, COTA/L, Barberton, OH.

THE CLEAN GAME

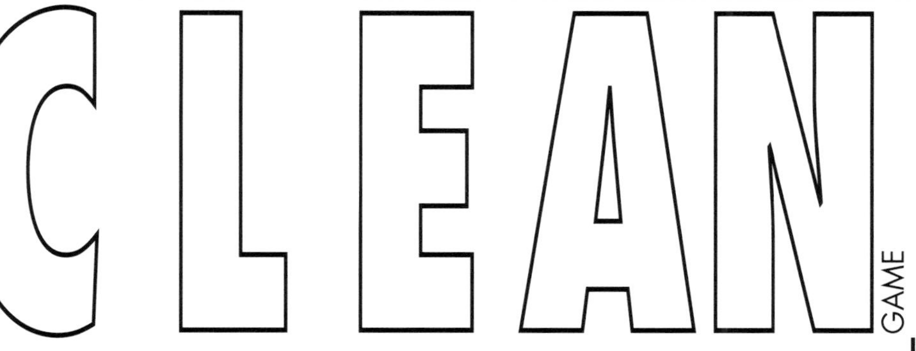

Cut each square along the perforated line.
Throw away the center square.

		FREE SPACE		

after-shave lotion	comb	cotton ball	cotton swab	dental floss
deodorant	foot powder	hairbrush	hair conditioner	lotion
makeup	mirror		mouthwash	nailbrush
nail clipper	nail file	shampoo	shaving cream	soap
talcum powder	toothbrush	toothpaste	towel	washcloth

THE  GAME

I. PURPOSE:

To increase awareness and independence with grooming and hygiene.

II. GENERAL COMMENTS:

Proper grooming and hygiene contribute to positive self-esteem and self-image. Poor grooming and hygiene are often indicators of depression, low self-esteem, decreased motivation and lack of initiative and/or concentration. It can affect people and the surrounding environment on a daily basis. It may also be an indicator of lack of knowledge, awareness or skills in this area. If a person becomes aware of these areas s/he is more likely to improve on them.

III. POSSIBLE ACTIVITIES:

This handout can be used in conjuction with GROOMING AND HYGIENE (page 51).

A. 1. Prior to playing the game, create facilitator *call-cards* by photocopying five sheets of the right side of the "CLEAN Game" activity sheet. Mark each of the twenty-four perforated boxes on the first page with a letter "C", each of the perforated boxes on the second sheet with an "L", the third sheet "E", the fourth sheet "A", and the fifth sheet "N". Cut the boxes apart (twenty-four from each sheet) discarding the free square. (You will have one hundred and twenty, one inch by one inch, squares of paper.) Mix them up in a hat or other container.
2. Photocopy one activity sheet for each member of the group.
3. Ask the group members to cut the page in half at the line with the scissors and then cut out the perforated squares with the pictures, discarding the free square.
4. Instruct each to glue or tape these squares anywhere on the card marked CLEAN except for the center "free square".
5. Offer group members the option of coloring in the word CLEAN (with markers, crayons or colored pencils) as well as the pictures.
6. Hand out twenty-five bingo tokens (or use paper clips, pennies, etc.) to each player, instructing each to cover the free square.
7. The caller picks a card from the hat, announcing the letter and item, for example, "L — toothbrush".
8. Each player that has a toothbrush, under the "L" column, covers his/her toothbrush.
9. When a player has completed a full row down, across, diagonal, or all four corners, s/he has won.
10. Ask the winner to discuss the purpose of each item that s/he covered.
11. Depending on the time, end play or continue playing, allowing for more winners.
12. Distribute a hygiene item of choice as a prize to winner(s).
13. Process by discussing the importance of good grooming and hygiene.

B. 1. Collect newspapers' ads sections, local catalogs, mailers, etc., that are advertising grooming/hygiene products.
2. Prior to group, enlarge each of the perforated boxes from the right side of the sheet on the photocopier and tape to a piece of cardboard.
3. Hold one card up in front of the group, asking from what type of store this item can be purchased.
4. Then ask for guesses on pricing of this item, marking them on chalkboard.
5. Ask the group members to go through the ads that were brought in, to find matching items.
6. Instruct them to cut out matching items and paper clip them to the card with the same item, with the price and the name of the store. Acknowledge the group members who have the best guesses.
7. Brainstorm ways of purchasing these items in the most affordable way, e.g., coupons, trading with friends, sales, sample sizes, off-brands, etc.
8. Process the activity by discussing the importance and affordability of the suggested items.

Activity handout and facilitator's information adapted from submission by Laura M. Grogan, OTR/L, Washington, D.C.

defining CHALLENGES

LET'S TALK TERMS!

IMPAIRMENT In the context of health experience, an impairment is any loss or abnormality of psychological, physiological or anatomical structure of function.*

In simpler terms, it is an illness, injury or disease.

What is your diagnosis, illness or problem? ____________________

____

How do you define your diagnosis, illness or problem? ____________________

____

Who told you about it or how did you learn about it? ____________________

____

DISABILITY In the context of health experience, a disability is any restriction or lack (resulting from an impairment) of ability to perform an activity in the manner or within the range considered normal for a human being.*

In simpler terms, how one's impairment affects his or her ability to function in different tasks and social roles.

How does your impairment affect your life? ____________________

____

How do you cope with limitations? ____________________

____

What changes have you made in your lifestyle because of your impairment? ____________________

____

HANDICAP In the context of health experience, a handicap is a disadvantage for a given individual, resulting from an impairment or disability, that limits or prevents the fulfillment of a role that is normal (depending on age, sex and social and cultural factors) for that individual.*

In simpler terms, how other people restrict you because of what they think about your impairment or disability.

How do others view you, or treat you? ____________________

____

What attributes or behaviors do they respond to? ____________________

____

How can you educate them about your impairment or disability? ____________________

____

* World Health Organization (1980). International classification of impairments, disabilities & handicaps: A manual of classification.

defining CHALLENGES

I. PURPOSE:

To combat the stigma of impairments, disabilities and handicaps by understanding each definition.

To identify how an illness affects an individuals' ability to function in activities of daily life.

II. GENERAL COMMENTS:

People often receive diagnostic labels that they do not understand. It is valuable to define terms so that everyone involved with a consumer/client is *on the same page* and speaking the same language. Beyond explaining medical terms, it is important to consider how other people may restrict an individual from doing certain activities because of certain beliefs about an illness. This sensitive topic is often under-discussed, but needs to be addressed to empower consumers/clients and their families/significant others. In addition, as healthcare professionals, it is important to use the correct terms, and be a role model for consumers/clients and families. This handout serves as a guideline for possible in-services, workshops and/or sensitivity training.

III. POSSIBLE ACTIVITIES:

A. 1. Prior to an individual or group meeting, instruct the consumer/client(s) to complete the handout.

2. Meet with the individual(s) in a 1:1 or group setting. Offer additional information as needed, e.g., about diagnostic categories, as well as identifying behaviors that may not fit into a specific diagnosis.

3. Give *homework assignments* such as:
   reviewing an article or book on the diagnostic group
   setting goals for participating in treatment
   keeping a journal about specific behaviors related to the diagnosis
   asking for feedback from other clients
   staff or family/significant others to identify what they see as part of the *illness*
   keeping a journal about how the illness affects daily activities or how others respond or treat him/her

B. 1. Prepare for a family support group by asking that consumers/clients come to the group one-half hour before the scheduled time with others.

2. Instruct group members to complete handouts honestly, knowing that they will be sharing this information with families/significant others at a later time.

3. After everyone has competed the handout, explain the topics discussed in the above stated GENERAL COMMENTS.

4. Welcome the families/significant others and ask that the consumer/clients explain the purpose of today's group, recalling previous discussion.

5. Divide group into clusters of families/significant others to review the handout together. Provide any needed information via book lists, suggested readings, resources, support groups, etc.

6. Process the group by asking what was helpful for consumers/clients and what was helpful for families/significant others.

Activity handout and facilitator's information adapted from submission by K. Oscar Larson, OTR, MA, Alexandria, VA.

PEOPLE WITH MENTAL ILLNESS ENRICH OUR LIVES

Abraham Lincoln

Beethoven

Patty Duke

Robert Schumann

LEO TOLSTOY

John Keats

Edgar Allan Poe

Isaac Newton

Michelangelo

Charles Dickens

PEOPLE WITH MENTAL ILLNESS ENRICH OUR LIVES

PURPOSE:

I. To combat the stigma of mental illness by acknowledging a list of high-achieving, creative and productive people who had/have a mental illness.

To assist in the process of illness-acceptance by identifying positive qualities that often accompany a mental illness.

II. GENERAL COMMENTS:

The actions of individuals, employers, family members, friends and society in general, are often reactions to the stigma of mental illness. In order to obliterate the stigma, the attitude about mental illness needs to change. Each individual needs to make strides toward that goal by understanding the truths about mental illness.

One example of an attitude change that will occur as people become more educated, is that people won't fear the mentally ill persons because of their being dangerous. The media perpetuates an image that mentally ill persons are violent, or victims of violence. The truth is that "the vast majority of mentally ill persons are not dangerous". (The Stigma of Mental Illness, National Institute of Mental Health, U.S. Dept. Health and Human Services, 1990)

Another change that will happen is a sensitivity to language and labels. Slang words like 'psycho' and 'nuts' are demeaning and inappropriate references to ill people.

A very important change that will occur is that persons with mental illness will not feel embarrassed, ashamed or apologetic for their illness and be able to ask for, and accept the help they need. Taking a look at the mentioned individuals in this handout is an excellent starting point for providing a sense of optimism and hope.

III. POSSIBLE ACTIVITIES:

A. 1. Distribute handouts to all group members. Provide a discussion of the above stated GENERAL COMMENTS.

2. Using page 54 as a resource, read together and discuss each persons' contribution.

3. Ask group members the following questions:

   Which of these peoples' names do you recognize?

   What specific characteristics, traits, skills, talents, and/or accomplishments do you admire/respect?

   What do you think these people had to overcome in order to accomplish what they did?

4. Provide feedback to group members about the uniqueness of each individual and allow for group support.

B. 1. Provide information in above stated GENERAL COMMENTS. Encourage open discussion.

2. Ask group members for names of people heard or read about who have a mental illness. List on chalkboard.

3. Distribute handouts and discuss how many the group was familiar with. Use page 54 for biographical data.

4. Problem solve ways to decrease the stigma of mental illness, such as not using slang words like 'psycho' or 'schizo', or by educating those family members or friends with whom they are comfortable, about the truths of mental illness.

5. Consider the benefits of a family support group, discussing these topics with the group members. Plan accordingly.

6. Process by discussing what qualities the listed people have in common. If these same qualities are noticed in group members, offer this feedback, conveying a sense of hope and optimism.

7. As an ongoing exercise, ask group members to add to the list of *People With Mental Illness Enrich Our Lives.*

Activity handout and facilitator's information submitted by Myron Jaffe, advocate. "People With Mental Illness Enrich Our Lives" poster, notecards and postcards are available from Wellness Reproductions Inc. For information call 800/669-9208.

CONVERSATION SKILLS

IS WHERE IT'S AT!

Sometimes, when we first meet people, it's difficult to start up a good conversation. What to talk about? What not to talk about? How often do you . . .

	ALWAYS	SOMETIMES	NEVER
Face and look directly into the eyes of the person you are talking to.			
Avoid overusing "I". (Sometimes people talk a lot about themselves because they're nervous.)			
Make sure you focus and listen when the person responds.			
Try bringing up something that's neutral – weather, recent movies or TV shows, current events, etc.			
Try to be honest, but not too honest. (Honesty is a good quality in relationships, but it can be overdone.)			
Give sincere compliments.			
Accept compliments by saying "Thank You".			
Avoid touchy subjects, like religion, politics or overly personal information from your past.			
End a conversation with a pleasant phrase - "Nice meeting you", "Hope to see you again", "It's been nice talking to you", etc.			

Looking at the marks above, which do you do best in conversations? ______________________

Which area do you feel you need to work on the most? ______________________

Conversation skills, like all skills, take time and practice. GIVE IT A TRY!

Conversation Skills

I. PURPOSE:

To increase communication by improving conversation skills when first meeting people.

II. GENERAL COMMENTS:

Effective conversation skills are helpful, if not vital in a variety of settings, such as work, social and even in treatment settings. Many people feel awkward when meeting people for the first time, sometimes out of nervousness, lack of positive experiences, low self-esteem, etc. The skill of starting up a good conversation eases a first encounter and can be a fun and non-threatening skill to learn in a group setting. It is important to recognize that first impressions do last and that first encounters often make or break relationships.

III. POSSIBLE ACTIVITIES:

A. 1. Introduce topic in above stated GENERAL COMMENTS.

2. Distribute handouts and review the nine friendly guidelines.
3. Write potential social situations on index cards that the group might encounter, such as day treatment program, singles group, self-help/support group, bowling club, church/temple, work, parties, civic groups, etc. Be specific in the description, e.g., *you are at a party from church and someone you don't know asks you who you are and what you are doing there.* Try and touch on the skills outlined in the handout. Ask each group member to write one situation, if able.
4. Explain to the group that everyone is encouraged to do at least one role-play to learn the skills outlined AND to have fun!
5. Distribute one index card per group member and proceed with role-plays.
6. Offer feedback on skills observed.
7. Process the group by asking group members what specific skill each group member will remember after the group is finished.

B. 1. Explain the topic briefly.

2. Ask which behaviors each group member would like and would not like to see when first meeting someone. Make a list on the board.
3. Distribute the handouts and compare the list on the board with the handouts' list.
4. Engage the group in a discussion of the following:

   When do we overuse "I"?
   How can we tell that we have talked about ourselves too much?
   What are certain topics to try to remember as neutral topics?
   What is good body language when first meeting someone?
   What is a good physical distance between people?
   What does "active listening" mean?
   How can we show people that we are "actively listening" to what they are saying?
   What is too honest in a first meeting?
   When do we tend to negate or slough off compliments? Why do we do that?
   What are certain topics to avoid in a first meeting?
   What information would you NOT share in a first encounter?
   What are common signals that tell you a conversation is ending?

5. Ask group members to write inside the arrow, in ranking order, what skills they most need to work on (the skill that needs the most work is "1", the skill that least needs work is a "9").
6. Process the group by discussing groups' commonalities or differences as well as potential places/situations to work on these important skills.

Listening Skills

IS WHERE IT'S AT!

Listening is a major part of a healthy communication process and an important skill. How would you rate your listening skills? How often do you . . .

	ALWAYS	SOMETIMES	NEVER
Put aside what you're doing.			
Focus your eyes on the speaker.			
Think about what the speaker is really saying.			
Avoid 'stepping on the other person's words'.			
Show interest with facial & body gestures.			
Respond with a non-judgmental attitude.			
Ask interested questions, remembering points for next discussion.			
Try not to overdo when bringing your own experiences into the discussion.			

Looking at the marks above, which do you do best as a listener? ____________________

Which area do you feel you need to work on the most? ____________________

Listening skills, like all skills, take time and practice. GIVE IT A TRY!

LISTENING SKILLS

I. PURPOSE:

To increase communication by improving listening skills when engaged in conversation.

II. GENERAL COMMENTS:

Effective listening skills are helpful in every situation throughout each person's day. They enable one to understand what is being told to them, have healthy relationships, be a part of group, etc. The skill of listening, opposed to just "being there" when someone is talking, is an important tool to acquire. "Active listening" requires not only hearing the words but also hearing the feelings behind the words, seeing the situation through the eyes of the speaker and not judging the speaker.

III. POSSIBLE ACTIVITIES:

A. 1. Introduce topic in above stated GENERAL COMMENTS.

2. Distribute handouts and review the eight listening hints.

3. Prior to the group write possible situations on index cards. A few might be: *"You ask a relative how they are feeling and they proceed to tell you, for the next 15 minutes"*, *"Your best friend has a devastating problem and discusses it with you"*, *"You meet someone nice at the store and they start a conversation with you"*, etc. Ask each group member to write one situation, if able.

4. Explain to the group that everyone is encouraged to do at least one role-play. This helps to learn the skills outlined AND to have fun!

5. Place cards face down in a hat and ask two people to pick one and role-play, one being the speaker and the other being the listener. After each person has done one role-play, encourage the pair to pick another card, reversing the roles.

6. Offer feedback on observed listening skills.

7. Ask group members to mention some friends, family members and professionals whom they feel have excellent and/or poor listening skills, encouraging them to give an example of how that person listens, and how they feel when this occurs.

8. Process by asking what skills group members would like to improve on and note if there are commonalities or differences.

B. 1. Explain the topic of listening.

2. Distribute handouts and discuss the eight listening hints.

3. Decide on a topic that could be a lively group discussion, e.g., a current event, a movie, or a controversial subject such as capital punishment, etc.

4. Form subgroups of three or four and blindfold each group member. Instruct the group to discuss the chosen topic for five minutes amongst themselves.

5. Take off the blindfolds and discuss another topic for five minutes.

6. Process the activity by asking group members to discuss how it felt to listen without seeing faces and expressions, and then with, noting the difference.

To be able to cope with an illness, it is important to understand the illness!

The purpose of this handout is to learn about **bipolar disorder (manic-depressive disorder)** in an effort to make healthy decisions.

The symptoms of bipolar disorder include manic and depressive episodes. Current terminology for manic-depressive disorder is bipolar disorder. The disorder is often described as an emotional roller-coaster.

In a **manic episode**, a person's mood is elevated, expansive or irritable. This must be different from a person's typical mood. The change must be unusually intense and must last for a considerable period. The manic episode may include the following symptoms to a significant degree.

1. Inflated sense of self-importance
2. Less need for sleep
3. Hyper-talkative
4. Flight of ideas or racing thoughts
5. Distractibility
6. Increase in physical activity
7. Over involvement in potentially harmful or risky behaviors (e.g., overspending, sexual behavior unusual for the person).

Oftentimes, psychosis is observed with delusions and hallucinations.

The **depressive episode** involves lack of interest or pleasure in activities.

The depressive episode may include the following symptoms:

1. Sleeping more or less than usual
2. Appetite changes
3. Difficulty in concentrating
4. Aches and pains with no physical cause
5. Suicidal thoughts and/or attempts
6. Feeling sad, worthless or guilty without cause

The symptoms may develop over a period of a couple of weeks, or may come on quite suddenly, especially if external factors involving stress (such as a death, divorce, etc.) were involved. The disturbance is severe enough to affect performance in work, self-care, social activities or relationships or to necessitate hospitalization. BIPOLAR DISORDER IS A MEDICAL ILLNESS.

Treatments for bipolar disorder vary, but as with most illnesses, is easiest when it's begun early.

Common treatment methods include:

medication therapy, (psycho)therapy and electroconvulsive therapy (ECT).

Many healthcare professionals are involved in the treatment of bipolar disorder:

psychiatrists, psychologists, occupational therapists, social workers, nurses, counselors, recreation therapists as well as other specialists who each bring something unique to the treatment process.

To help you cope with some of the complications of bipolar disorder, it is important to know ways to make your life run smoother.

What are some ways you either know now, or would like to learn?

1. ______________________ 2. ______________________

3. ______________________ 4. ______________________

A **TOXIC ENVIRONMENT** is unhealthy and includes elements that might precipitate symptoms.

A **SUPPORTIVE ENVIRONMENT** is a situation that allows you to function at your very best.

TOXIC ENVIRONMENT	SUPPORTIVE ENVIRONMENT

RECOMMENDED RESOURCES:

______________________ ______________________

______________________ ______________________

You are not alone! Over 1% of the population has bipolar disorder!
Recognize the symptoms, know where to get help and take the actions you need to!

coping with bipolar disorder

coping with bipolar disorder

I. PURPOSE:

To increase knowledge of consumers (as well as families, significant others and all those interested and concerned) about bipolar (manic-depressive) disorder.

II. GENERAL COMMENTS:

The facts about serious mental illness are often hard to find - especially in a brief, user-friendly format. It is important to empower all of the individuals involved with a serious mental illness (the consumers themselves and/or their family/significant others) with education, supportive interactions and appropriate choices. It is advisable to proceed with caution as the listeners (consumers and/or family members) need to be able and ready to hear this information.

III. POSSIBLE ACTIVITIES:

A. 1. Distribute handouts in a family support group setting.
2. Review handout together as a group.
3. Provide discussion of coping skills - using leisure skills, relaxation, exercise, effective communication skills, realistic expectations, good sleep hygiene, etc.
4. Discuss the components of a toxic/supportive environment with the group members, e.g., Toxic: Being overly criticized, Being overly controlled. Supportive: Safe or accepting environment, Freedom to express feelings and needs.
5. Instruct each family unit to meet for five minutes to discuss and write the individual's "ways to make life run smoother" and "components of environments" as outlined on the front of the handout. Compare as a group.
6. Provide recommended resources along with additional bibliographical references as needed, encouraging group members to write information on handout.
   Example: "Manic-Depression - Voices of an Illness" audiotape, available from Wellness Reproductions Inc., 800 / 669-9208.

> NAMI (National Alliance for the Mentally Ill) – Helpline – 800 / 950-NAMI
>
> NARSAD (National Alliance for Research on Schizophrenia and Depression) – 516 / 829-0091

7. Discuss the disorder openly, providing the most recent information on new or experimental drugs. Emphasize the importance of compliance with the prescribed medication regimen even when feeling stable. Include a discussion of the stigma of mental illness, if appropriate.
8. Offer support and information as needed.
9. Process by asking group members what was learned, emphasizing that it is important that both consumer and family members' needs are met.

B. 1. Offer this handout as a 1:1 session with individuals who have been diagnosed with bipolar disorder.
2. Review handout with consumer, as needed, providing requested information.
3. Discuss what coping skills are and what a "toxic environment" might be:
   a. chaotic and noisy living conditions
   b. lack of personal rights
   c. temptations to use alcohol or drugs

   Then discuss what a "supportive environment" might be:
   a. calm and orderly living conditions
   b. atmosphere where one can assert rights
   c. protection from temptation
4. Instruct individuals to evaluate personal coping skills and environments and to complete the appropriate sections.
5. Assist in setting appropriate goals to learn coping skills and to optimize a supportive environment.
6. Provide recommended resources to assist in completing recommended resources section.
7. Suggest that family/significant others be included in the education process.
8. Process by reviewing information and goals.

coping with major depressive disorder

To be able to cope with an illness, it is important to understand the illness!

The purpose of this handout is to learn about **major depressive disorder** in an effort to make healthy decisions.

There are many types of depression.
A **major depressive disorder** is characterized by a *depressed or 'empty' mood.* It often involves:

- a *loss of pleasure* in activities.
- a *weight gain or loss* when not dieting and a *decreased appetite.*
- *sleep pattern changes, restlessness, irritability,* or a *loss of physical activity, tiredness* or a *loss of energy.*
- *feeling of worthlessness and hopelessness,* excessive or inappropriate *guilt.*
- a lack of ability to *think clearly – difficulty concentrating, remembering* or making *decisions.*
- recurrent *thoughts of death,* a *suicidal plan* or a *suicidal attempt.*
- *aches and pains* with no physical cause.

To be a major depression, the illness does not need to be caused by another illness and does not need to be a typical reaction to the loss of a loved one. Major depression is typically severe enough to affect social or occupational activities. The symptoms may develop over a period of a couple of weeks or may come on quite suddenly, especially if external factors involving stress (such as death, divorce, etc.) are involved. MAJOR DEPRESSIVE DISORDER IS A MEDICAL ILLNESS.

Treatments for major depression vary, but as with most illnesses, is easiest when it's begun early.

Common treatment methods include:

medication therapy, (psycho)therapy, cognitive therapy and electroconvulsive therapy (ECT).

Many healthcare professionals are involved in the treatment of major depression:

psychiatrists, psychologists, occupational therapists, social workers, nurses, counselors, recreation therapists as well as other specialists who each bring something unique to the treatment process.

To manage your depression, it is important to know ways to make your life run smoother.

What are some ways you either know now, or would like to learn?

1. ____________________ **2.** ____________________

3. ____________________ **4.** ____________________

A **TOXIC ENVIRONMENT** is unhealthy and includes elements that might precipitate symptoms.
A **SUPPORTIVE ENVIRONMENT** is a situation that allows you to function at your very best.

TOXIC ENVIRONMENT	SUPPORTIVE ENVIRONMENT

RECOMMENDED RESOURCES:

____________________ ____________________

____________________ ____________________

You are not alone! 5% of the population has major depression!

Recognize the symptoms, know where to get help and take the actions you need to!

coping with major depressive disorder

I. PURPOSE:

To increase knowledge of consumers (as well as families, significant others and all those interested and concerned) about major depressive disorder.

II. GENERAL COMMENTS:

The facts about serious mental illness are often hard to find - especially in a brief, user-friendly format. It is important to empower all of the individuals involved with a serious mental illness (the consumers themselves and/or their family/significant others) with education, supportive interactions and appropriate choices. It is advisable to proceed with caution as the listeners (consumers and/or family members) need to be able and ready to hear this information.

III. POSSIBLE ACTIVITIES:

A.
1. Distribute handouts in a family support group setting.
2. Review handout together as a group.
3. Provide discussion of coping skills - using leisure skills, relaxation, exercise, effective communication skills, realistic expectations, good sleep hygiene, etc.
4. Discuss the components of a toxic/supportive environment with the group members, e.g., TOXIC: Being overly criticized, Being overly controlled. SUPPORTIVE: Safe or accepting environment, Freedom to express feelings and needs.
5. Instruct each family unit to meet for five minutes to discuss and write the individual's "ways to make life run smoother" and "components of environments" as outlined on the front of the handout. Compare as a group.
6. Provide recommended resources along with additional bibliographical references as needed, encouraging group members to write information on handout.

> NAMI (National Alliance for the Mentally Ill) – Helpline – 800 / 950-NAMI
>
> NARSAD (National Alliance for Research on Schizophrenia and Depression) – 516 / 829-0091

7. Discuss the disorder openly, providing the most recent information on new or experimental drugs. Emphasize the importance of compliance with the prescribed medication regimen even when feeling stable. Include a discussion of the stigma of mental illness, if appropriate.
8. Offer support and information as needed.
9. Process by asking group members what was learned, emphasizing that it is important that both consumer and family members' needs are met. Inform group members that depression is one of the more treatable diseases.

B.
1. Offer this handout as a 1:1 session with individuals who have been diagnosed with major depressive disorder.
2. Review handout with consumer, as needed, providing requested information.
3. Discuss what coping skills are and what a "toxic environment" might be:
   a. negative, unmotivated and/or angry people
   b. inability to express self / lack of personal rights
   c. temptations to use alcohol or drugs

   Then discuss what a "supportive environment" might be:
   a. spending time with people who have positive energy, direction and goals
   b. atmosphere where one can assert rights
   c. protection from temptation
4. Instruct individuals to evaluate personal coping skills and environments and to complete the appropriate sections.
5. Assist in setting appropriate goals to learn coping skills and to optimize a supportive environment.
6. Provide recommended resources to assist in completing recommended resources section.
7. Suggest that family/significant others be included in the education process.
8. Process by reviewing information and goals.

coping with schizophrenia

To be able to cope with an illness, it is important to understand the illness!

The purpose of this handout is to learn about **schizophrenia** in an effort to make healthy decisions.

Schizophrenia is a complicated brain disorder characterized by a variety of symptoms. The symptoms vary from individual to individual in intensity, nature and frequency.

Positive symptoms refer to:

- Distorted reality - perceptions of the world might be interpreted in a way other than intended or different from how others would perceive the same situation.
- Delusions - false beliefs or thoughts not grounded in reality, e.g., persecutory, grandoise
- Hallucinations - false perceptions, e.g., hearing voices or seeing nonexistent things
- Disordered thinking - thoughts are loose and seem illogical, incoherent talk

Negative symptoms refer to the lack or absence of certain behaviors:

- Poor concentration
- Blunted emotions - the world seems flat or unreal and reactions are at times inappropriate or lacking
- Lack or absence of initiative, motivation, interests and enjoyment.
- People with schizophrenia often experience a decline in work, self-care and social relations.

Negative symptoms are more difficult to treat with medications than positive symptoms are at this time.

There are different types of behavior within schizophrenia including paranoid, catatonic, disorganized, undifferentiated and residual. Schizophrenia can appear suddenly or develop gradually. SCHIZOPHRENIA IS A MEDICAL ILLNESS.

Treatments for schizophrenia vary, but as with most illnesses, is easiest when it's begun early.

Common treatment methods include:

medication therapy, (psycho)therapy and occasionally electroconvulsive therapy (ECT).

Many healthcare professionals are involved in the treatment of schizophrenia:

psychiatrists, psychologists, occupational therapists, social workers, nurses, counselors, recreation therapists as well as other specialists who each bring something unique to the treatment process.

To help you cope with some of the complications of schizophrenia, it is important to know ways to make your life run smoother.

What are some ways you either know now, or would like to learn?

1. ______________________ **2.** ______________________

3. ______________________ **4.** ______________________

A **TOXIC ENVIRONMENT** is unhealthy and includes elements that might precipitate symptoms.
A **SUPPORTIVE ENVIRONMENT** is a situation that allows you to function at your very best.

TOXIC ENVIRONMENT	SUPPORTIVE ENVIRONMENT

RECOMMENDED RESOURCES:

______________________ ______________________

______________________ ______________________

You are not alone! Approximately 1% of the population has schizophrenia!
Recognize the symptoms, know where to get help and take the actions you need to!

coping with schizophrenia

I. PURPOSE:

To increase knowledge of consumers (as well as families, significant others and all those interested and concerned) about schizophrenia.

II. GENERAL COMMENTS:

The facts about serious mental illness are often hard to find - especially in a brief, user-friendly format. It is important to empower all of the individuals involved with a serious mental illness (the consumers themselves and/or their family/significant others) with education, supportive interactions and appropriate choices. It is advisable to proceed with caution as the listeners (consumers and/or family members) need to be able and ready to hear this information.

III. POSSIBLE ACTIVITIES:

A. 1. Distribute handouts in a family support group setting.
2. Review handout together as a group.
3. Provide discussion of coping skills - using leisure skills, relaxation, exercise, effective communication skills, realistic expectations, good sleep hygiene, etc.
4. Discuss the components of a toxic/supportive environment with the group members, e.g., Toxic: Being overly criticized, Being overly controlled. Supportive: Safe or accepting environment, Freedom to express feelings and needs.
5. Instruct each family unit to meet for five minutes to discuss and write the individual's "ways to make life run smoother" and "components of environments" as outlined on the front of the handout. Compare as a group.
6. Provide recommended resources along with additional bibliographical references as needed, encouraging group members to write information on handout.
   Examples: Surviving Schizophrenia, by E. Fuller Torrey, M.D., "Voices of an Illness" audiotape and "Schizophrenia - Surviving in the World of Normals" – "A Love Story - Living With Someone With Schizophrenia" videotape, all available from Wellness Reproductions Inc., 800 / 669-9208.

   NAMI (National Alliance for the Mentally Ill) – Helpline – 800 / 950-NAMI
   NARSAD (National Alliance for Research on Schizophrenia and Depression) – 516 / 829-0091

7. Discuss the disorder openly, providing the most recent information on new or experimental drugs. Emphasize the importance of compliance with the prescribed medication regimen even when feeling stable. Include a discussion of the stigma of mental illness, if appropriate.
8. Offer support and information as needed.
9. Process by asking group members what was learned, emphasizing that it is important that both consumer and family members' needs are met.

B. 1. Offer this handout as a 1:1 session with individuals who have been diagnosed with schizophrenia.
2. Review handout with consumer, as needed, providing requested information.
3. Discuss what coping skills are and what a "toxic environment" might be:
   a. loud, noisy nights
   b. lack of personal rights
   c. temptations to use alcohol or drugs

   Then discuss what a "supportive environment" might be:
   a. quiet, restful nights
   b. atmosphere where one can assert rights
   c. protection from temptation
4. Instruct individuals to evaluate personal coping skills and environments and to complete the appropriate sections.
5. Assist in setting appropriate goals to learn coping skills and to optimize a supportive environment.
6. Provide recommended resources to assist in completing recommended resources section.
7. Suggest that family/significant others be included in the education process.
8. Process by reviewing information and goals.

DON'T LET LAUNDRY GET YOU DOWN!

USE THESE HELPFUL HINTS TO STAY AHEAD OF THE GAME:

	I knew this and I do it!	I knew this, but I don't do it.	I didn't know this... I'll try it!
✦ Know your machines and what options they might have. Washing cycles will help save fabrics and water levels. Temperature controls help save money.	☐	☐	☐
✦ Read the washing instructions on all of your clothes first.	☐	☐	☐
✦ Be sure everything's out of the pockets.	☐	☐	☐
✦ Zip zippers, button the buttons, make sure no cords or strings are untied.	☐	☐	☐
✦ Repair all rips or torn off buttons to keep clothes looking their best.	☐	☐	☐
✦ Use a stain remover whenever tough spots occur as soon as possible, even if you don't plan on washing the article right away.	☐	☐	☐
✦ Wash whites with whites only. Wash like colors together.	☐	☐	☐
✦ Wash heavy fabrics, like jeans, together.	☐	☐	☐
✦ Wash bright colors and dark colors in cold to prevent fading or colors running onto each other.	☐	☐	☐
✦ Wash clothes that have fabric paint, decals, beads, sequins or prints inside-out to prevent them from wearing or falling off.	☐	☐	☐
✦ Hang clothes on a line whenever possible. This will make your clothes last longer.	☐	☐	☐
✦ Do not overdry or dry on too hot of a setting. This prevents shrinking.	☐	☐	☐
✦ Fold clothes immediately after they dry to avoid wrinkling.	☐	☐	☐
✦ ____________________	☐	☐	☐
✦ ____________________	☐	☐	☐

Choose one or two days each week to do your laundry. Consistency assists you in keeping your laundry from getting backed-up without feeling as if you're doing laundry constantly.

SUNDAY	MONDAY	TUESDAY	WEDNESDAY	THURSDAY	FRIDAY	SATURDAY

Don't let LAUNDRY get you down!

I. PURPOSE:

To increase home management skills by learning how to take care of one's clothes.

II. GENERAL COMMENTS:

Appearance generally reflects how one feels. When clothes are stained, dirty, torn, wrinkled or shrunk, it can be indicative of self-esteem and affect it as well. Getting the laundry done correctly and done when needed can be overwhelming and stressful. Providing basic laundry tips may assist in home management and may influence self-care. (Inform or remind participants that are parenting, that there are benefits of children doing, or helping, with the laundry. The youngsters can learn to group or classify objects by sorting. Such activities aid the development of logical thinking skills and teach them how to follow a sequence of directions.)

III. POSSIBLE ACTIVITIES:

A. 1. Compile a laundry basket of clothes of different fabrics, styles, colors, weights, etc.
2. As a group, ask the patients to decide which articles of clothing could be washed together, placing them in piles.
3. Distribute handouts.
4. Read each laundry tip together as a group, discussing whether these tips were known before and whether these tips were followed. Add any additional tips that the group members suggest to the bottom of the list.
5. Instruct the group to look at the pile of clothes that was put together initially and make changes as needed.
6. Complete the last section of the handout by having group members pick a day or days to do laundry, discussing why those days were chosen.
7. Process the activity by discussing what group members learned or were reminded of, and what had been forgotten.

B. 1. Distribute handouts.
2. Read each tip together as a group.
3. Ask group members to highlight or check off the tips that will be most helpful.
4. Encourage members to share personal laundry tips with the group and to write the helpful ones on the list.
5. Using a dry erase board, draw a line down the middle, labeling one side "SELF-ESTEEM" and the other side "TIME MANAGEMENT".
6. Ask group members to brainstorm on how clean, well-taken-care-of clothes can increase self-esteem and time management. (Group members may copy these on the back of handouts.)
7. Complete the last section, asking group members to pick a day or days that each plans to do laundry.
8. Process this activity with discussion of results of which skill is viewed as being the most helpful.

Activity handout and facilitator's information adapted from submission by Teresa A. Bachtel, COTA/L, Barberton, OH.

No matter how much money you're making, it seems like it's never enough. Here's some ideas...

HOW TO STRETCH YOUR BUDGET

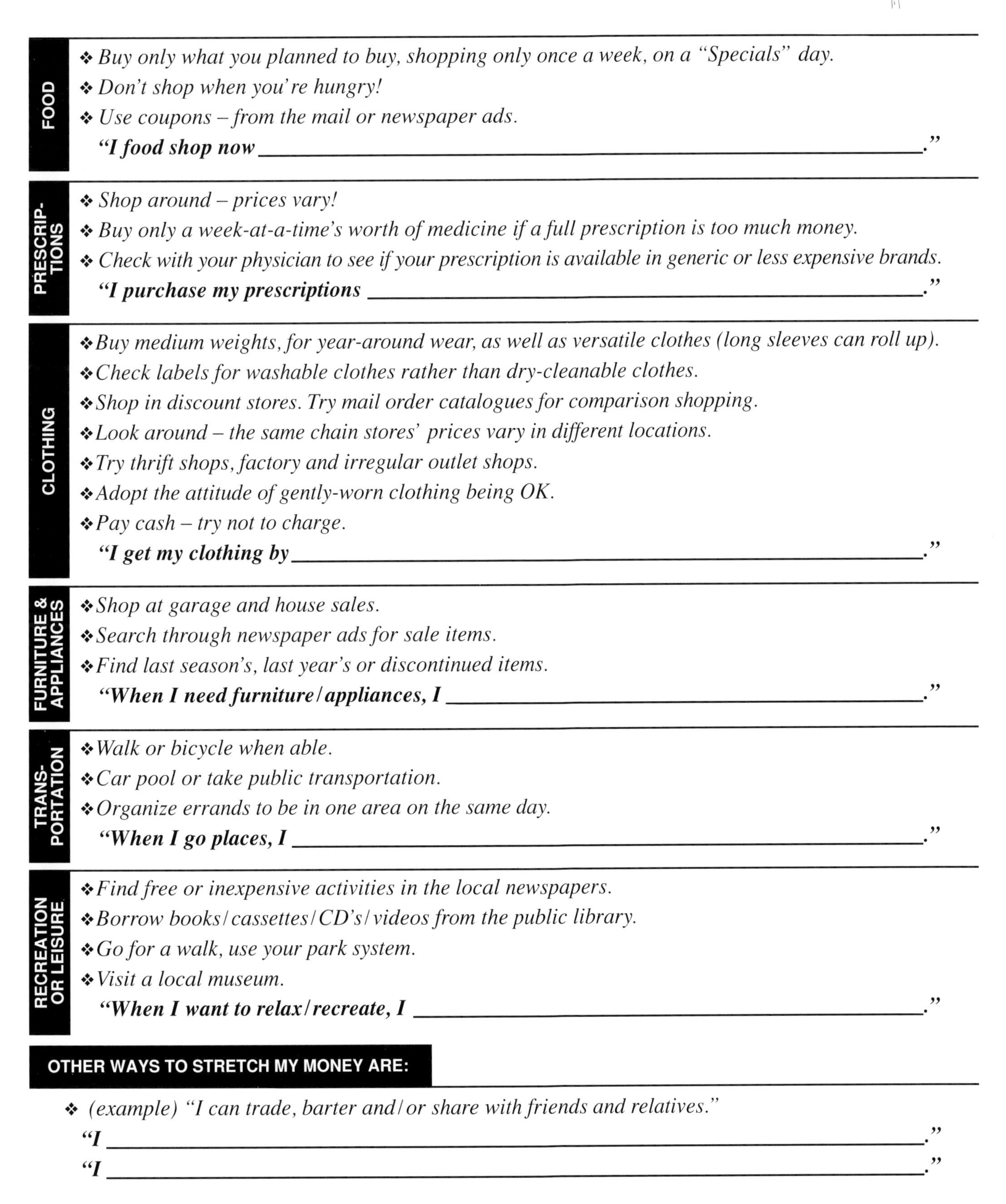

FOOD

- ❖ *Buy only what you planned to buy, shopping only once a week, on a "Specials" day.*
- ❖ *Don't shop when you're hungry!*
- ❖ *Use coupons – from the mail or newspaper ads.*

"I food shop now ____."

PRESCRIPTIONS

- ❖ *Shop around – prices vary!*
- ❖ *Buy only a week-at-a-time's worth of medicine if a full prescription is too much money.*
- ❖ *Check with your physician to see if your prescription is available in generic or less expensive brands.*

"I purchase my prescriptions ______________________________________."

CLOTHING

- ❖ *Buy medium weights, for year-around wear, as well as versatile clothes (long sleeves can roll up).*
- ❖ *Check labels for washable clothes rather than dry-cleanable clothes.*
- ❖ *Shop in discount stores. Try mail order catalogues for comparison shopping.*
- ❖ *Look around – the same chain stores' prices vary in different locations.*
- ❖ *Try thrift shops, factory and irregular outlet shops.*
- ❖ *Adopt the attitude of gently-worn clothing being OK.*
- ❖ *Pay cash – try not to charge.*

"I get my clothing by ____."

FURNITURE & APPLIANCES

- ❖ *Shop at garage and house sales.*
- ❖ *Search through newspaper ads for sale items.*
- ❖ *Find last season's, last year's or discontinued items.*

"When I need furniture/appliances, I __________________________________."

TRANSPORTATION

- ❖ *Walk or bicycle when able.*
- ❖ *Car pool or take public transportation.*
- ❖ *Organize errands to be in one area on the same day.*

"When I go places, I ____."

RECREATION OR LEISURE

- ❖ *Find free or inexpensive activities in the local newspapers.*
- ❖ *Borrow books/cassettes/CD's/videos from the public library.*
- ❖ *Go for a walk, use your park system.*
- ❖ *Visit a local museum.*

"When I want to relax/recreate, I __________________________________."

OTHER WAYS TO STRETCH MY MONEY ARE:

- ❖ *(example) "I can trade, barter and/or share with friends and relatives."*

"I ____."

"I ____."

HOW TO STRETCH YOUR BUDGET

I. PURPOSE:

To increase money management skills by learning ways to stretch a budget and to plan ahead.

To gain insight and awareness of present personal spending habits.

II. GENERAL COMMENTS:

Most people are reluctant to discuss their personal financial situation, particularly in a group situation. However group members may be receptive to identify the universal problem of the dollar not going very far, and will welcome assistance in figuring out how to stretch it further. Planning ahead before purchasing takes time and effort, but is beneficial, and can be financially and emotionally rewarding.

III. POSSIBLE ACTIVITIES:

A. 1. Distribute handouts, reviewing and discussing each section, asking group members to complete open-ended statement at the end of each section.

2. Instruct members to list on the back of the page the last two places where each one last shopped. Ask group members to write one item purchased from each store and the approximate amount that was paid.

3. Going around the room, ask each person to share what the listed items were and to think of a way of obtaining that same item, of adequate quality, at a more affordable price.

4. After each person's comments, facilitate discussion of additional ways to save money.

5. Process by asking each group member to list the three best suggestions of stretching the dollar that was learned from this group.

B. 1. Distribute handouts, reviewing and discussing each section, asking group members to complete open-ended statement at the end of each section.

2. Ask each group member to choose one category (food, prescriptions, clothing, furniture & appliances, transportation, recreation or leisure) and list on the back of the handout probable purchases during the next week.

3. Facilitate discussion of attempting to stretch the dollar without compromising the quality of the products, as well as discussing the importance of moderate quality of products.

4. Instruct group to problem solve each item listed, discussing how and where each purchase could be made in order to stretch the dollar the furthest, still maintaining adequate quality.

5. Process by discussing the potential benefits of planning ahead.

6. For further skill development, ask each group member to develop a plan of all of the next week's probable purchases. Instruct each to bring the plan to the group at the next session.

EASY-WAYS to fix a meal!

When we have low energy,
it's hard to muster up enthusiasm for cooking.
So, we are going to find a way to eat healthy
and preserve our energy.

Rules:
1. EASY-WAYS have 6 or less ingredients.
2. EASY-WAYS use no more than 2 pots, pans or bowls.
3. EASY-WAYS take no more than 10 minutes from start to finish!

Optional Melts — EASY-WAY Recipe

1 slice bread or English muffins	2 medium tomatoes, thinly sliced
2 slices of part-skim Mozarella cheese	salt and pepper to taste
Optionals: sliced turkey or chicken / onions and/or other vegetables	

Set oven control to broil. Place bread on rack in broiler pan.

Broil with tops about 4 inches from heat until golden brown; turn.

Place optional on bread and broil until warmed.

Place cheese on bread slices, broil until cheese begins to melt.

Arrange tomatoes on cheese. Sprinkle with salt and pepper.

Baked French Toast — EASY-WAY Recipe

4 large eggs	1/2 tsp. vanilla extract & ground cinnamon
1 cup 1% milk	8 slices of white or Italian bread
Possible Toppings: Powdered sugar, cinnamon, jelly, maple syrup or fresh fruit	

Preheat oven to 350 degrees.

Beat eggs. Add milk, vanilla extract and cinnamon to the eggs. Mix well.

Soak the sliced bread in the egg mixture for about 5 minutes, until it is absorbed.

Arrange bread on a nonstick baking sheet.

Bake for approximately 15 minutes until the bread is slightly brown.

____________ EASY-WAY Recipe

____________ EASY-WAY Recipe

~ Pass your EASY-WAY ideas around to others who might need them - and enjoy fixing meals ... the EASY-WAY! ~

EASY-WAYS to fix a meal!

I. PURPOSE:

To increase the ability to plan, prepare and eat nutritious meals during low-energy level periods.

II. GENERAL COMMENTS:

It is important to learn to conserve energy, especially when in recovery from an illness or a traumatic event. We need to give ourselves permission to prepare nutritious meals in an affordable manner, without making a mess or expending a lot of energy. Meal preparation does not need to be complicated, it can be done in an EASY-WAY!

III. POSSIBLE ACTIVITIES:

A.
1. Explain concept as discussed in above stated GENERAL COMMENTS.
2. Distribute handouts and review.
3. Ask group members to write personal recipes in bottom two "index cards".
4. Photocopy bottom section of each group member's handout for each member of the group making an "EASY-WAY COOKBOOK".
5. If group members give permission, keep the recipes on file for future groups.
6. Process the importance of conserving energy, prioritizing and learning survival skills in an effort to heal ourselves.

B.
1. Give group a list of six or less common, affordable ingredients, such as: eggs or egg-substitutes, bread, milk, low-fat oil, salt, and pepper. Explain clearly the criteria for an "EASY-WAY" as stated on the front of the handout.
2. Ask group members to brainstorm all the "EASY-WAY" recipes they can come up with in 5-10 minutes. (Divide into teams making a game if the group is large enough.)
3. Discuss as a group.
4. Distribute handouts and ask group members to complete handout.
5. Vote as a group, selecting one or two recipes the group members would like to prepare for a meal. Plan accordingly, including shopping list, budget, coupons, etc., setting a date for the cooking group.
6. Photocopy bottom section of each group member's handout, making an "EASY-WAY COOKBOOK" to distribute to each member.
7. Process by discussing the benefits of "EASY-WAY" cooking and of sharing and/or exchanging information.

Imagine that you are stocking a kitchen for yourself... list the items you would purchase, assuming that you already have the regular staples (flour, sugar, vinegar), spices and condiments (e.g., mustard, mayonnaise, pepper).

REFRIGERATOR	FREEZER	CUPBOARD
example: milk	*example:* heat/serve macaroni & cheese	*example:* dry cereal

With the items stocked, menu plan for yourself for:

	ONE DAY THAT YOU FEEL MODERATELY GOOD	TWO DAYS THAT YOU FEEL LOW IN MOOD/ENERGY	
		Day 1	Day 2
breakfast:			
lunch:			
supper:			

Menu Planning

I. PURPOSE

To identify healthy food choices.

To plan for healthy eating, taking into account energy level.

II. GENERAL COMMENTS

Humans run on fuel that helps to improve immune system function and maintain energy level. It is helpful to plan ahead for those times that one does not have the interest or decision-making power to plan at the last minute.

III. POSSIBLE ACTIVITIES:

A. 1. Introduce topic of nutrition / healthy eating choices.

2. Provide education about basic food groups, recommended daily allowances, etc.
3. Distribute handouts asking group members to identify the types of foods that may be healthy and tasty to stock a kitchen.
4. Instruct individuals to plan full-day menus for themselves, taking into account energy level.
5. Encourage participants members to share low-energy day ideas.
6. Process the benefits of making healthy food choices and of planning ahead.

B. 1. Introduce topic of nutrition / healthy eating.

2. Distribute handouts with color pencils, markers or pens, asking group members to complete the top portion.
3. Instruct participants to indicate their current kitchen stock in one color.
4. Facilitate discussion regarding ways to make grocery shopping and eating enjoyable and manageable.
5. Using another color have participants add to the list, balancing out the ingredients, thereby creating a shopping list.
6. Instruct group members to plan full-day menus for themselves, taking into account energy level.
7. Process benefits of this activity.

Activity handout and facilitator's information submitted by Erika Pond Clements, B.Sc. O.T. (c), Burlington, ON, Canada.

HUMOROUS STORY STARTERS

Humor is an incredibly valuable coping skill! Use it or lose it!

Write in your "Story Starters" captions or create talking ( ) or thinking ( ) bubbles.

" ______________________________ "

" ______________________________ "

" ______________________________ "

" ______________________________ "

HUMOROUS STORY STARTERS

I. PURPOSE:

To increase humor by using creative thinking and writing skills to see the funny side of life.

II. GENERAL COMMENTS:

Funny things happen all around us, even to us, all the time. Unfortunately, life gets very serious sometimes and we can't always see the humorous side. Humor is a wonderful coping skill and has been very effective in dealing with serious illnesses of all kinds. The "Story Starters" are one way to promote creativity, humorous thinking and fun interaction.

III. POSSIBLE ACTIVITIES:

A. 1. Distribute handouts.

2. Explain "Story Starters" as a way to get the *creative juices* flowing.
3. Do one "Story Starter" together as a group. Ask group for captions to one of the cartoons, e.g., number 1: "Boy, the last one is slow!", "Nice turtles always finish last!", "When I said you needed to develop a thicker skin, I didn't think you'd go so far!" and "There's always one kid in the group!"
4. Ask each group member to write a caption or to create cartoon bubbles for the other three cartoons and share as a group.
5. Involve group in story telling, by asking each group member to tell one story about an event that they thought of, or remembered, because of seeing a cartoon in this activity.
6. Process by discussing the emotional and physiological benefits of laughing, sharing and using humor in everyday life to cope with stress.

B. 1. Explain the concept of using humor as a coping skill.

2. Distribute handouts.
3. Divide group into four subgroups, assigning a different cartoon to each group.
4. Ask each group to create five questions about their cartoon, e.g., in the duck picture:
   What is the duck thinking?
   What are the duck siblings thinking?
   What is the turtle saying?
   What would a typical father duck say, if he saw his family coming home?
   What are the neighbors saying?
   Then, ask each group to give their set of questions to another group.
5. Instruct each group to answer the five questions using creativity and humor.
6. Share as a group, promoting laughter and fun.
7. Process by discussing the benefits of looking at the humorous side of life and finding the time and energy to laugh by ourselves and with others, observing that while we're laughing, we're usually not hurting.
8. For further fun, ask group members to make comic strips by drawing three empty frames and use one of the "Story Starters" as a final punch line frame.

Take control of your life ...using HUMOR!

QUICK...Name one thing that will: reduce stress in your life, aid digestion, help you live longer, make you a more creative problem solver and add sparkle to your love-life and social encounters. Research shows that a sense of humor can do all that and MORE! When you laugh (or smile) at yourself or your situation, YOU TAKE CONTROL OF YOUR LIFE.

Here are 17 ways to lighten up and to improve your LAUGH-LIFE! Match up the examples in the right column to the tips in the left.	
1. Smile more. __D__	A. where you can hang up tabloids, cartoons from the newspapers, funny pictures, etc.
2. Try to laugh at your problems more. _______	B. You'll find a whole humor section in your favorite bookstore. Pick one. Or two!
3. Keep a funny, 365 page calendar in your kitchen or car. _______	C. Play part of the tape another time for yourself, for family and/or associates.
4. Use a fun poster, mug, button, T-shirt and signs that say things like: _______	D. Smiles help you look younger and make others wonder what you really know!
5. Make a collection of toys and share them with co-workers, friends and family. Toys help break the ice, inducing playfulness and laughter. _______	E. lean over to turn on the bathtub faucet and get doused by the shower. Or when you wait 1/2 hour at the bakery and then realize that you need to take a number!
6. Tape a late night comedy show. _______	F. Share your jokes with someone else.
7. Keep a box of crayons and blank paper handy. _______	G. "Enjoy life, this is not a dress rehearsal".
8. Listen to different music. Sing a lot. _______	H. popcorn to share with others.
9. Keep a book of humor. _______	I. Hang around with others that make you laugh.
10. Write down a joke you've heard or tear one out from a magazine or paper. _______	J. Each day, when you tear off the page, leave it where others can see it and write a note to a friend.
11. Have at least one 'game' you can play. _______	K. NEWSFLASH! "How to lose 10 pounds a week eating chocolates" ... "3 week old child has twins" ...etc.
12. Spend at least a half hour each week in a gift store. _______	L. When you laugh at problems and inconsistencies, even though life may be unjust, you're in control.
13. Try to laugh at yourself & see the funny side of a situation, like when you: _______	M. Teddy bear, slinky, yo-yo, train whistle, hand puppets and a bubble blower.
14. Collect and hang up the "best" of the Tabloid newspapers. _______	N. Doodle or scribble. Be creative!
15. The next time you go to a meeting bring .... _______	O. Read funny greeting cards!
16. Set up a HUMOR BULLETIN BOARD. _______	P. Playing cards, board and/or word games, puzzles.
17. Be sensitive with whom you spend time. _______	Q. Play holiday music all year round. Try carousel music.

SOMEDAYS YOU'RE THE BUG. SOMEDAYS YOU'RE THE WINDSHIELD. HOW YOU CHOOSE TO RESPOND IS UP TO YOU!

17 ways to improve your Laugh-LIFE

I. **PURPOSE:**

To use humor as a stress management and coping tool.

To identify 17 ways to bring some control into life when stressful situations arise.

II. **GENERAL COMMENTS:**

Humor and laughter are two metaphors for: Joy, Peace, Happiness, Love, Optimism, Friendship, Inspiration, Hopefulness, Playfulness, Creativity, Compassion, Sense of Purpose, Support, Determination, Celebration and The Will to Live. For the most part it is an underdeveloped stress management and coping skill.

III. **POSSIBLE ACTIVITIES:**

A. 1. Distribute handouts and ask each participant to complete. Utilize answer box below if needed.
2. Discuss which of the 17 suggestions were liked best by each person.
3. Ask participants what stressors each person is feeling in her/his work and/or personal life.
4. Explore how each of the activities can be used to bring some CONTROL into each of their lives using one of the 17 suggestions to control one of their stressors.
5. List how many other humor activities participants are already using or would like to use.
6. Process by developing realistic Laugh-Life action plans.

B. 1. Present these quotations to the group:
a. *"The best way to cheer yourself is to cheer someone else up."*
– Mark Twain, writer
b. *"We all live with the objective of being happy: our lives are all different and yet the same."*
– Anne Frank, writer
c. *"Most folks are about as happy as they make up their minds to be."*
– Abraham Lincoln, 16th president of the United States
d. *"Happiness depends on ourselves."*
– Aristotle, philosopher
e. *"Frame your mind to mirth and merriment, which bars a thousand harms and lengthens life."*
– William Shakespeare, poet and dramatist
2. Discuss personal meanings of each quote, asking participants if the quotes provide any insight into the person who wrote them. Emphasize to participants that these quotations are from many years ago and that this concept has been around a long time.
3. Distribute handouts and ask each participant to complete. Utilize answer box below if needed.
4. Instruct participants to set goals using one or two ideas from the handout to improve their Laugh-Lives and share with the group.
5. Process by discussing the variety of benefits of a healthy Laugh-Life.

Answers:						
	1. D	4. G	7. N	10. F	13. E	16. A
	2. L	5. M	8. Q	11. P	14. K	17. I
	3. J	6. C	9. B	12. O	15. H	

Activity handout and facilitator's information adapted from submission by
John F. Murphy, M.Ed. and Ann M. Murphy, M.Ed., Hingham, MA.

A Better View of INTERVIEWS

DEFINITION: *meeting of two people face to face, as for questioning and evaluating a job applicant; obtaining and giving information; two or more persons talking with the definite purpose of exchanging facts related to hiring.*

You have arrived ON TIME at the interview, ready to present yourself as being calm, collected and qualified. Being correctly groomed helps you to maintain your confidence and self-esteem. The first impression you have created will help to convince the interviewer that you are valuable.

PERSONAL APPEARANCE CHECK LIST

APPLICANT IS A: (CIRCLE ONE) MALE or FEMALE

AT THIS MOMENT:
Evaluate your personal appearance.
Is it appropriate for an interview?

AT AN INTERVIEW:
What should I wear?
What can I do to make a good first impression?

[*Ex: jeans - not appropriate* — PANTS/TROUSERS/SHORTS/JEANS — *Suit gives better impression.*]
[*Ex: gum, eating, smoking - not appropriate* — TEETH — *Brush teeth, use mouthwash.*]

________ **PANTS/TROUSERS/SHORTS/JEANS** ________
________ **SUIT/DRESS/SKIRT** ________
________ **SHIRT/BLOUSE/T-SHIRT** ________
________ **SOCKS/STOCKINGS/SHOES** ________
________ **HAIR** ________
________ **TEETH** ________
________ **HANDS** ________
________ **FRAGRANCE/MAKE-UP** ________
________ **JEWELRY** ________
________ **CARRIER FOR PERSONAL PAPERS** ________

COMMON INTERVIEW QUESTIONS

Tell me about yourself. ________
What are your greatest strengths and weaknesses? ________
Why do you want to work for us? ________
What kind of salary are you looking for? ________
What do you know about our company? ________
Why should we hire you? ________
What are your long-term goals? ________
What were your most rewarding experiences in your previous jobs? ________
Who can we contact as a reference? ________
Do you prefer to work alone or in a group? ________
Are you a team player? ________
Tell me about a conflict you have dealt with and how you resolved it. ________
What are your previous work experiences? ________

THE BIG FINISH

Do you have any questions to ask us? ________

FOLLOW-UP

1. ________ 2. ________ 3. ________

A Better View of INTERVIEWS

I. **PURPOSE:**

To increase job readiness by improving skills needed for successful interviewing.

II. **GENERAL COMMENTS:**

The job interview is a more or less formal discussion between an employer and a potential job candidate. It is an exchange of ideas about the nature of the job and the candidate's qualifications. Employers search for certain traits in a potential employee. It is important that the potential employee knows what to expect and what is expected of him/her and feels prepared.

III. **POSSIBLE ACTIVITIES:**

A. 1. Before group session, using magazines and/or catalogues, clip illustrations of different types of clothing, both casual and business. Glue or staple each illustration onto a piece of cardboard.

2. Distribute handouts. Read top of handout aloud. Facilitate discussion of importance of creating a positive first impression. Show illustrations of clothing, asking group members to verbally categorize the clothing as appropriate, or not appropriate, for a job interview.

3. Instruct group members to complete left side of "Personal Appearance Checklist" based on their present style of dress and grooming, as if they were going to a job interview immediately after the session. (Ask group members if clothing items are appropriate, or not appropriate, for a job interview.)

4. Brainstorm possible solutions/alternatives to present choice of dress. Ask group members to imagine what an interviewer would be looking for in a prospective employee. Complete right side of handout.

5. Facilitate discussion of what to expect at a job interview and importance of being prepared. Allow ten minutes to complete "Common Interview Questions".

6. Ask group members, one at a time, to share written responses. Encourage feedback and discussion of responses.

7. Discuss importance of section labeled "The Big Finish".

8. Lead group discussion on questions to be asked of an interviewer.

9. Brainstorm possible follow-up activities to a job interview, e.g., handshake, written thank-you note, follow-up phone call, etc.

10. Process activity by discussing groups' feeling of being more prepared for an interview.

B. 1. Before group session, cut apart "Common Interview Questions" in strips, fold and place in a basket.

2. Distribute handouts and facilitate discussion of importance of first impressions at a job interview.

3. Instruct group members to complete handout.

4. Divide group into pairs and ask each pair to pick one interview question from the basket.

5. Elicit volunteers to role-play their question, one person sitting behind a desk/table, the other sitting, facing the other person on the opposite side of the desk/table.

6. If time allows, ask group members to write additional interview questions and role-play.

7. Process activity by discussing the importance of being prepared to answer interview questions.

Activity handout and facilitator's information adapted from submission by Elaine M. Hyla, M.Ed., Euclid, OH.

Starting Your Job Search

You're ready to enter or reenter the world of work. Rarely does a job come looking for you. More likely, you'll have to do the looking. Finding the right job can be a full-time job in itself. Where do you start?

Zero in on the things you like to do and are best able to do.
List your strengths, accomplishments, responsibilities, hobbies, sports, clubs, interests, leadership positions. Think about positive qualities that others have told you about yourself, e.g., artistic, punctual, dependable. Match them to an employment opportunity that might appeal to you.

	POSITIVES I KNOW ABOUT MYSELF	APPEALING EMPLOYMENT
EX:	*Cooking*	*Restaurant*
1.		
2.		
3.		
4.		

How do you handle stress? Do you get along with other people? Is it difficult for you to get out of bed early in the morning? Can you keep a secret? Being on the path to a successful job search means taking inventory of not only your skills but also being honest about which areas you might need additional training or self-awareness. Use the spaces provided below to list these areas. Which potential jobs might be too challenging? Recognize the whole truth about yourself.

	OTHER TRUTHS I KNOW ABOUT MYSELF	UNAPPEALING EMPLOYMENT
EX:	*Problem balancing checkbook*	*Being a bank teller*
1.		
2.		
3.		
4.		

Even if you've never received a paycheck, *you still have experience*. Inventory each job/responsibility you've held. What was positive and what was negative about the experiences?

	JOB RESPONSIBILITY	(+)	(–)
EX:	*PTA Room Parent*	*Organizing phone committee*	*Driving in bad weather*
1.			
2.			
3.			
4.			

What you do well won't stop when you begin work. It would be safe to assume that you will get better at what you do well. You might even get better at what you don't do well right now. Your possibilities are endless!

Starting Your Job Search

I. **PURPOSE:**

To assist in a successful job search by using the self-inventory method.

II. **GENERAL COMMENTS:**

In order to ease the transition from the role of potential applicant to a responsible employee, it is helpful to assess strengths and weaknesses, create a checklist, then match talents and abilities to potential employers.

III. **POSSIBLE ACTIVITIES:**

A. 1. Bring to the group the "Help Wanted" section from a recent newspaper. Clip ads for positions that a group member could fill, e.g., retail clerk, restaurant host/hostess, file clerk, cook, cashier, factory worker, etc. Glue or tape ads onto a sheet of paper and photocopy enough for each person.

2. Distribute photocopies of want ads to group. Facilitate discussion of *positives* required by potential employers as listed in "Help Wanted" ads.

3. In order to increase insight of existing *positives*, ask group members to think about the activities at which each has experienced a level of comfort or success. Facilitate discussion. Some examples are:

Volunteer work Organizational skills *(meet deadlines, plan ahead, solve problems, etc.)*
House/Handy work Manual Dexterity *(build, assemble, follow a recipe, repair, etc.)*
Home Finances Deal with numbers/data *(keep records, manage money, organization, etc.)*
Personal Relationships Work well with others *(peacekeeper in family, caregiver, conversationalist, etc.)*
Leadership Community/Church/Temple activities *(arrange social functions, motivate, run meetings, etc.)*
Expression Creativity, artistic skills *(dance, draw, write, music, sing, play instrument, etc.)*

4. Distribute handouts. Instruct group members to "inventory" *positives* by completing the section labeled "Positives I Know About Myself".

5. Complete section by matching an appealing employment opportunity to each *positive* in the first column.

6. Read middle section of handout aloud. Instruct group members to complete.

7. Instruct each group member to complete bottom section of handout. Process activity with discussion of potential effect of activity on one's employment future.

B. 1. Obtaining the local Sunday newspaper's "Help Wanted" section, clip enough descriptive ads for every member of the group, plus one for role playing. Glue or tape each onto an index card.

2. Distribute handouts. Discuss the paragraphs in the top (*positives*) and middle (*other truths*) sections. Ask group members to fill in the left column only in those two sections.

3. Discuss ways in which carefully reading the "Help Wanted" ads can be advantageous to the job applicant to ascertain whether the job suits the individual, e.g., motivated, courteous, experience, flexible, location, early or late hours, etc.

4. Distribute an index card to each person and ask them to see if that particular ad fits under the "appealing" or "unappealing", next to their *positives* or *other truths*.

5. Pass index cards around a few times, asking group members to do the same with each card.

6. Ask each group member to take another look at the *positives* and *other truths* they had listed and decide if there are others that could be added to the list, after reading the "help wanted" ads.

7. Instruct group members to complete the bottom part of the handout.

8. Process activity by discussing the impact that self-inventory activities have upon a job search.

Activity handout and facilitator's information adapted from submission by Elaine M. Hyla, M.Ed., Euclid, OH.

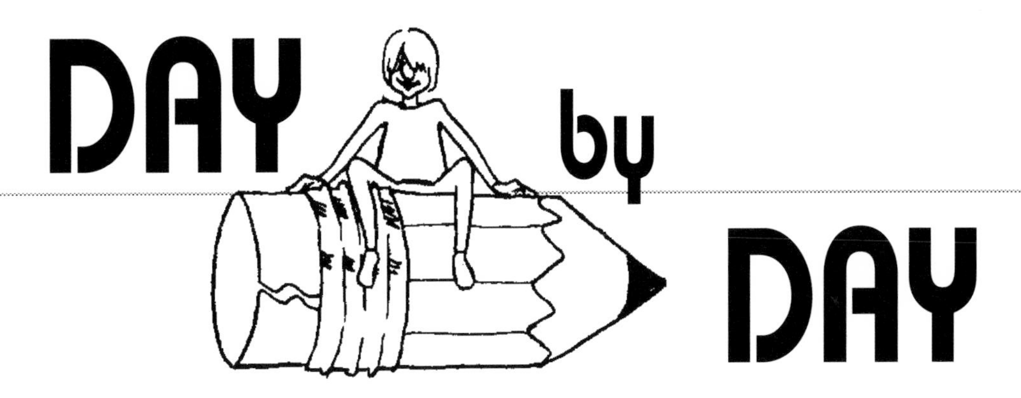

SELF-NURTURING JOURNAL of ______________________

(Name)

One way to improve your self-esteem is to do something for yourself everyday and let yourself appreciate it. Because you may not be accustomed to doing something for yourself, it may feel strange, or impossible to do, but keep it for at least one full week to start to retrain yourself. It does not need to be a big or time-consuming activity, just as long as it is something that you do because you choose to do so.

Date and Situation	How I felt
1)	
2)	
3)	
4)	
5)	
6)	
7)	

PERSONAL STRENGTHS JOURNAL of ______________________

(Name)

One way to improve your self-esteem is to recognize the strengths that help you to do the things you do every day and let yourself appreciate them. Because everyone has good days and bad days, and no one can achieve huge successes every day, it may sometimes seem hard to recognize your strengths. Persist and be sure to appreciate even the seemingly little things every day!

Date and Situation	Strengths Involved
1)	
2)	
3)	
4)	
5)	
6)	
7)	

DAY by DAY

I. **PURPOSE:**

To use journalizing as a method to monitor and increase self-esteem.

II. **GENERAL COMMENTS:**

Here are two different but similar ways to increase self-esteem. The first is to spend special time regularly to nurture oneself. This also leads to higher energy level and improved ability to cope with stress. The second is to recognize one's strengths and accomplishments on a regular basis. Both ways can be developed as skills with practice, support and encouragement. Journalizing assists the process by noting progress and level of commitment. Depending on group needs and time availability, offer one or both halves of the handout.

III. **POSSIBLE ACTIVITIES:**

A. (For top activity)

1. Introduce concept of self-nurturance and how it relates to self-esteem.
2. Facilitate discussion around the impact of behavior on thoughts and feelings.

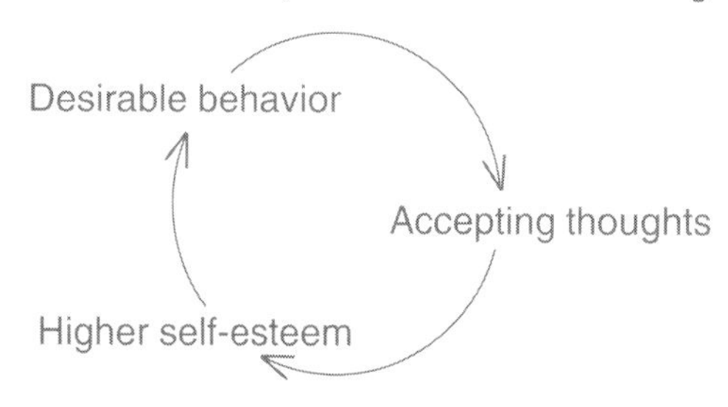

3. Ask participants to identify personal examples where each saw this positive cycle.
4. Brainstorm as a group, activities or behaviors that are self-nurturing.
5. Distribute handouts, offering the following examples, or using some from the group:

August 24	read an entertaining book for 1/2 hr.	interested, relaxed
August 25	made MY favorite meal for supper	satisfied, capable
August 26	ENJOYED my usual cup of tea	warm, cozy, relaxed

6. Ask participants to keep journal for one week to discuss at next meeting or in individual sessions.
7. Process by asking group members to summarize topic and purpose of this activity.

B. (For bottom activity)

1. Introduce topic of self-esteem and the importance of acknowledging one's accomplishments and strengths.
2. Distribute the handouts.
3. Use the following examples or one from the group:

Jan 22	I phoned a friend because I felt lonely.	self-awareness
Jan 23	I felt tired, so I took a hot bath and went to bed early.	self-caring, flexibility
Jan 24	I did laundry even though I didn't want to.	organization, discipline

4. Ask individuals to think back over previous week and identify one accomplishment and the personal strength(s) used.
5. Instruct the individuals to maintain this journal for one week and to take the issue of self-esteem day by day. The journals can be reviewed at the next group session or individually.
6. Process by discussing what the impact might be of recognizing strengths, especially on *bad days* when the awareness of strengths is needed the most.

Activity handout and facilitator's information adapted from submission by Erika Pond Clements, B.Sc.O.T.(c), Burlington, ON, Canada.

What have I been UP to??

It can be difficult to present yourself to others when you have been dealing with low mood, anxiety, illness or injury for some time. However, you can present yourself truthfully and positively with some thought and practice.

Identify some ways that you can truthfully deal with questions like: Where have you been lately? What have you been up to? When are you ready to start ______________ again? etc.

Some examples include the following, but add any other ideas you have (on the back).

1. *I have been dealing with ______________________________ over the past ________ days/weeks/months/years.*

2. *I have learned ______________________________ ______________________________ (about my mood/illness/health).*

3. *I am working on improving my mood/strength/health/______________ by: ______________________________.*

4. *It's amazing what a difference ______________________________ ______________________________ (health practices) are making for me.*

5. *An accomplishment I have had in the past week/month is ______________________________ ______________________________.*

6. *I know I am making improvements in ______________________________.*

7. *I have been told I am making improvements in ______________________________.*

8. *Something I am thinking about trying to help myself is ______________________________.*

I will write in my journal again on ______________________________.
(day, date, time)

By journalizing, you can monitor your progress and see yourself grow.

What have I been UP to??

I. PURPOSE:

To use a journal format to improve communication skills by developing positive self-portrayal statements.

To reframe defeating self-talk.

II. GENERAL COMMENTS:

Journalizing offers time to reflect and a concrete way to share with others. When faced with low self-esteem or low mood, individuals can present a negative image to themselves and others which can perpetuate itself. Reframing one's self evaluation can increase self-esteem, and help one to be more pleasant to be around, thus ensuring ongoing support and acceptance from others. This exercise emphasizes increasing self-esteem using writing and making affirmations aloud.

III. POSSIBLE ACTIVITIES:

A. 1. Introduce topic of talking to others (family, friends, employers, etc.) about one's illness or condition.

2. Discuss the effect of negative self-portrayal on relationships, support and acceptance from others.

3. Introduce the concept of reframing.

4. Explain that writing serves many purposes, for example, to see visually what was thought and to make commitments. Discuss other potential benefits.

5. Distribute handouts and ask group members to complete at least four of the reframing statements.

6. Explain the importance of hearing the written word aloud. Ask group members to share at least one self-portrayal statement.

7. Process by facilitating discussion of the likely reaction of those around each individual to this type of self-portrayal. Offer blank handouts to those interested, for continued journalizing. Encourage group members to read aloud what each wrote, to internalize statements.

B. 1. Ask group members to divide in pairs or triads and to role-play a conversation in which each answers questions about their health in their typical manner.

2. Discuss how it feels to be on either end of the conversation.

3. Reconvene as a large group.

4. Distribute handouts and ask group members to complete after explanation of purpose. Describe journalizing as a way to learn to reframe by slowing down, thinking before answering and looking at self-esteem issues. Facilitate discussion of positive affirmations and benefits.

5. Instruct each group member to read aloud emphasizing benefits of hearing ones' words, offering support as needed.

6. Regroup members into original pairs or triads and perform role-plays again - using this type of response to the same questions.

7. Process by discussing the differences between the reframed second experience and the first role-play.

8. Emphasize to group members that this type of personal growth requires practice. Distribute blank handouts, instructing group members to journal one time per week for two months and share with someone they trust.

Activity handout and facilitator's information adapted from submission by Erika Pond Clements, B.Sc.O.T.(c), Burlington, ON, Canada.

Write to Heal

There are many ways to heal.
One of them is to write – the art of journalizing.
Here are 2 different activities:

1. *LETTER OF TRAUMA SURVIVOR*

By releasing pent-up anger and guilt you are taking responsibility for your healing process.

Dear ____________________ ,

You ________________________ me on ____________________________.
I feel ____.
I think that you are _______________________________________.
I have ____.
I am not responsible for you hurting me.
The best thing I can tell you is that I am recovering from this.
You do not control me through this.
I have found support from __________________________________.

From, _________________________

2. *MY JOURNAL*

It's important to take time out for yourself. One way to do this is by keeping a journal. Set a time for yourself to jot down feelings, beliefs and actions. This will not only help you review the day, but also organize your thoughts. You may even learn something about yourself in the process! To get you going, a few idea-starters have been written below. This format can be used afterwards as you continue to write.

Date: ____________________

I felt ____
____ today.

I believed ____
____ today.

I did ____
____ today.

Remember - Take Responsibility - You Have the Right to Heal!

Write to *Heal*

I. PURPOSE:

To explore journalizing as a coping skill.
To take responsibility for healing by confronting the perpetrator in a constructive way.
To use journalizing to examine how thoughts, feelings and actions relate to each other.

II. GENERAL COMMENTS:

Sometimes thoughts, feelings and actions can be overwhelming. In order to gain perspective, it is often healing to write or journalize. The first activity provides a precise format for a trauma survivor to release pent-up anger and guilt that often impedes recovery. The structure suggests which areas are advisable to cover.

The second activity ties together how thoughts, feelings and actions interrelate. For some people, it is helpful to write in a journal, walk away from it and then come back and reread it, to gain clarity. Depending on group needs and time availability, offer one or both halves of the handout.

III. POSSIBLE ACTIVITIES:

This handout can be in conjunction with HEALING MEDITATION page 52.

A. 1. Distribute handouts. Explain to the group members that there are 2 activities; the first will most likely be more emotional than the second.
2. Ask the participants to think of their abuser. This will enable group members to complete the first activity.
3. Encourage the trauma survivors to write even though they may have no intention of mailing the letter. Explain to group members that by specifically stating what the abuser did and when, the survivor can begin the process of recovery.
4. Encourage exploration of the feelings of grief: anger, denial and depression.
5. Describe the purpose of the second activity and the importance of doing activities that support and help one gain insight. Instruct group members to complete the journal by the next session.
6. Provide support and encouragement to those group members who choose to read the letter aloud to the group.
7. Process by asking group members to describe any support available from agencies, individuals or groups to provide reassurance that "you are not alone".

B. 1. Open discussion of each individual's *right to heal.*
2. Distribute handouts explaining that one very effective way to heal is through writing. Allow group members to discuss previous experiences with writing.
3. Ask the participants to think of their abuser. This will enable group members to complete first activity.
4. Encourage the trauma survivors to write even though they may have no intention of mailing the letter. Explain to group members that by specifically stating what the abuser did and when, the survivor can begin the process of recovery.
5. Ask group members how each felt before and after writing using the EMOTIONS© handout/poster, Life Management Skills I, page 11. Instruct group members to share the letter with trusted friends/family after the group session.
6. Introduce next activity as a way to sort out thoughts and gain insight.
7. Use the following example or one from the group:

   Date: July 1

   I felt . . . lonely because no one called me.
   I believed . . . that no one cared about me because of my past.
   I did . . . something about it by calling a friend and asking her to visit.
8. Ask each group member to complete one journal entry.
9. Share as a group and process benefits of each writing project.

Activity handout and facilitator's information adapted from submission by Tamara Nance, MA, LPC, RNC, Hickory, NC.

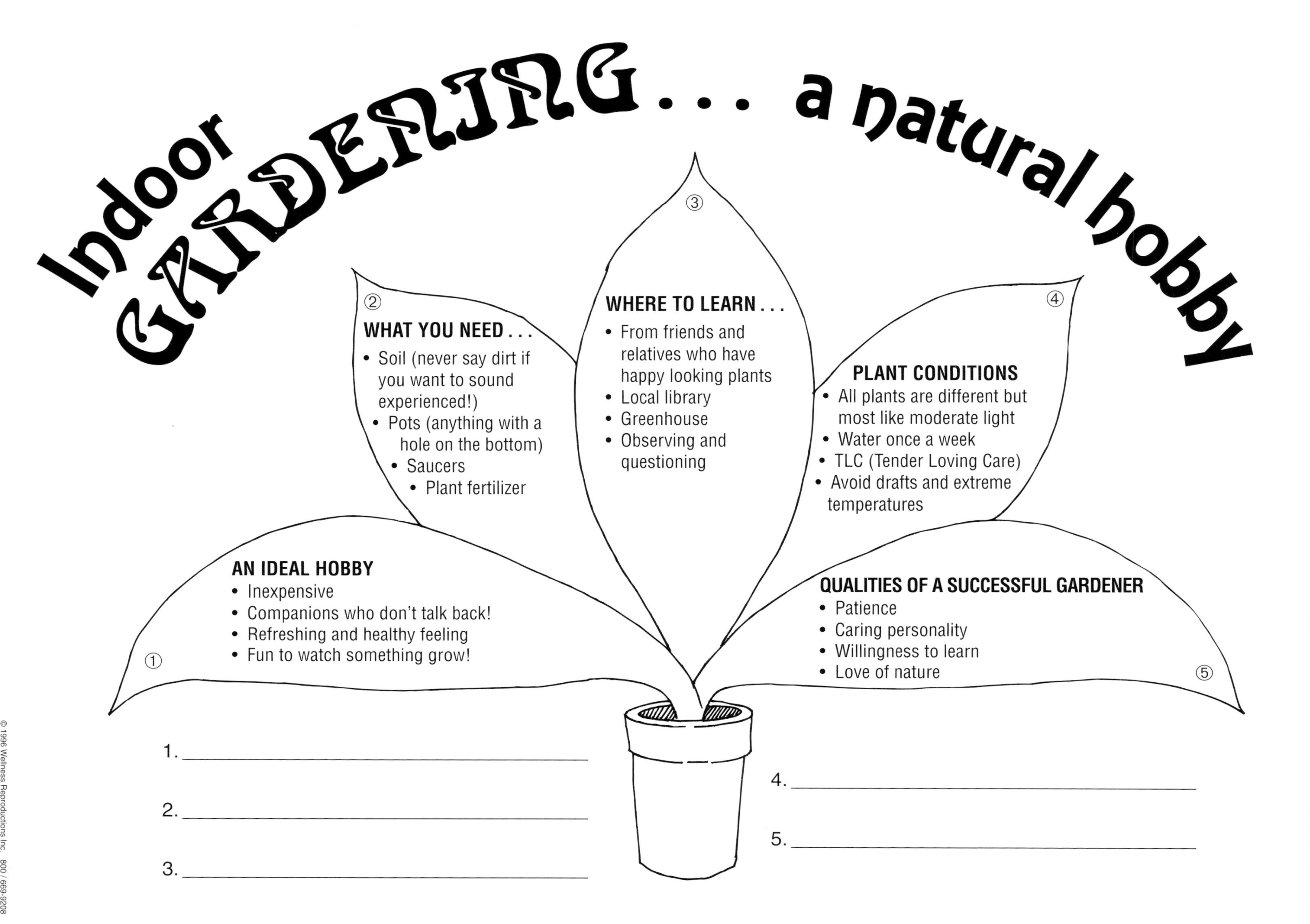
Indoor GARDENING . . . a natural hobby
①
AN IDEAL HOBBY
• Inexpensive
• Companions who don't talk back!
• Refreshing and healthy feeling
• Fun to watch something grow!
②
WHAT YOU NEED . . .
• Soil (never say dirt if you want to sound experienced!)
• Pots (anything with a hole on the bottom)
• Saucers
• Plant fertilizer
③
WHERE TO LEARN . . .
• From friends and relatives who have happy looking plants
• Local library
• Greenhouse
• Observing and questioning
④
PLANT CONDITIONS
• All plants are different but most like moderate light
• Water once a week
• TLC (Tender Loving Care)
• Avoid drafts and extreme temperatures
⑤
QUALITIES OF A SUCCESSFUL GARDENER
• Patience
• Caring personality
• Willingness to learn
• Love of nature
1. ____
2. ____
3. ____
4. ____
5. ____

Indoor GARDENING . . . a natural hobby

I. **PURPOSE:**

To introduce indoor gardening as a leisure skill.

II. **GENERAL COMMENTS:**

It is vital to establish leisure skills in all phases of life. Indoor gardening has a lot to offer! Connecting with nature in this way can be soothing, refreshing, exciting, calming, fulfilling, etc. Plants can be a comfort to people who are healing, likewise, there is something innately healing about tending to nature.

III. **POSSIBLE ACTIVITIES:**

A. 1. Elicit assistance from colleagues, asking for "plant cutting" contributions one week prior to the group. Put in water to root.

2. Give one cutting or small plant to each group member, instructing each how to plant and water properly.

3. Distribute handouts reviewing each section.

4. Ask the following five questions to group members. Instruct group members to fill in bottom of handout.

a. Where can you get cuttings or plants?

b. What supplies do you already have to begin gardening?

c. Who do you know that has plants?

d. Where in your home/apartment/room do you think a plant could grow?

e. What qualities do you have to be a successful gardener?

5. Instruct everyone to turn the handout over.

6. Process by asking group members, "What do you remember from this group meeting?"

B. 1. Distribute the handouts.

2. Divide the group into subgroups of five.

3. Ask each subgroup to brainstorm as many ideas as possible in five minutes to add to each leaf's list.

4. After five minutes discuss as a group. Ask group members to write a favorite idea from each subgroups' presentation on the bottom of the handout.

5. Discuss ways of starting this hobby within the next week.

6. Process by identifying benefits of this leisure skill and discuss how creativity can be explored after basic gardening skills are reviewed.

7. Explain that after basic gardening skills are acquired, other creative ideas can be explored, i.e., terrariums, decorating pots, macramé hangers, dried flower arranging, outdoor gardening, grafting, specialty plant collections (African violets), grafting, artificial plants, etc. Offer local resources' addresses and phone numbers.

The LEISURE LINK

"Your link to a healthier life"

LEISURE INTERESTS	DOES THIS INTEREST YOU?	CAN YOU AFFORD THIS?	WHAT DO YOU NEED TO DO BEFORE YOU BEGIN THIS ACTIVITY?
Play Cards • Board/Table Games			
Garden • Plants • Yardwork			
Woodworking			
Paint • Draw • Sketch			
Attend Concerts/Plays			
Attend/Rent Movies			
Listen to Music • Dance			
Camp • Fish • Hunt			
Golf			
Swim • Sunbathe			
Bowl			
Go to Parks • Hike • Picnic			
Exercise • Jog • Walk • Lift Weights			
Basketball • Baseball • Football • Volleyball			
Bicycling			
Travel/Vacations			
Socialize • Party • Visit People			
Crossword/Seek & Find Puzzles			
Video/Electronic Games			
Fairs • Circus • Zoo • Amusement Park			
Science/Art/History/Health Museums			
Write Stories/Poems/Journals			
Collecting			
Cook • Bake			
Read			
Sew • Knit • Embroider • Crochet			
Shop • Garage Sales • Flea Markets • Antiques			
Crafts • Models • Projects			
Church/Temple Activities			
Attend/Watch Sporting Events			
Home Decorate/Renovate			
Auto Racing/Mechanics			
Leatherwork			
Computer			
Volunteer			
Miscellaneous			
Others:			

Put an **"A"** *beside activities that you do alone. Put a* **"P"** *after the activities that require planning.*

The LEISURE LINK

I. PURPOSE:

To increase awareness of leisure activities and available community resources.

To determine feasibility of pursuing appealing leisure interests.

II. COMMENTS:

A healthy balance of one's schedule includes active leisure pursuits. At times, many people are in need of new leisure interests or reinvolving themselves with previous leisure activities. Choosing leisure activities can be tricky because it involves so many factors . . . Can I afford this? Do I have the time? Will this allow me quiet time? Will this connect me with other people? Does it require too much planning? Is it close enough for me to get there? Benefits of leisure are numerous! They include relaxation, self-improvement, having fun, meeting new people, taking risks, exercising, stimulating the mind, etc.

III. POSSIBLE ACTIVITIES:

A. 1. Photocopy handout and cut each leisure activity into a strip of paper.
2. Fold strips in half, place in a basket and ask each group member to pick one strip of paper.
3. Ask for a volunteer to act out chosen leisure activity as a charade, the other group members guessing the leisure activity.
4. When the group has correctly guessed, discuss together who might be interested in pursuing this activity.
5. Continue asking for volunteers until each person has had a turn. If time permits, continue until all activities have been played.
6. Process activity by discussing possible community resources.
7. Offer handout as homework assignment for next group session.

B. 1. Gather resource information prior to group, e.g., telephone books, pamphlets, brochures, coupons, advertisements, park brochures, sports page of newspaper, etc.
2. Photocopy handouts and distribute to each group member.
3. Instruct group members to complete handout individually.
4. Ask each member to share two or three leisure activities of interest.
5. Request that each member share one activity each would like to do but can't afford.
6. Problem solve as a group ways to see if there are solutions as to how it might be affordable, e.g., can't afford an electronic game, but can save up money and go to a video arcade once in a while.
7. Place resource information in center of the table and allow group members to look through, obtaining information each might need to implement activities.
8. Process activity with discussion of availability of resources for leisure activities.

Activity handout and facilitator's information adapted from submission by Bonny A. Reed-Bell, OTR/L, Canton, OH., Teresa A. Bachtel, COTA/L, Barberton, OH., and Pamela A. Joy, COTA/L, Canton, OH.

LEISURE SCAVENGER HUNT

Parks
Name & Phone #
1. ____________________
2. ____________________
3. ____________________

Name & Phone #
1. ____________________
2. ____________________
3. ____________________

Book/Music/Video Stores
Name & Phone #
1. ____________________
2. ____________________
3. ____________________

Amusement/Family Theme Parks
Name & Phone #
1. ____________________
2. ____________________
3. ____________________

Special Interests & Location
Name & Phone #
1. ____________________
2. ____________________
3. ____________________

Museums
Name & Phone #
1. ____________________
2. ____________________
3. ____________________

Recreation Classes
Name & Phone #
1. ____________________
2. ____________________
3. ____________________

Religious Groups/Organizations
Name & Phone #
1. ____________________
2. ____________________
3. ____________________

Movies & Theatres
Name & Phone #
1. ____________________
2. ____________________
3. ____________________

Lectures/Classes
Name & Phone #
1. ____________________
2. ____________________
3. ____________________

Game/Art/Hobby Stores
Name & Phone #
1. ____________________
2. ____________________
3. ____________________

FINISH

I. PURPOSE:

To identify constructive ways to use free-time.

To discover and develop individual leisure interests in one's community.

II. GENERAL COMMENTS:

This activity encourages the participants to become familiar with their community. It provides a means to explore community recreation and leisure resources while gathering a sense of spatial relationships between home and areas that provide recreational interests.

III. POSSIBLE ACTIVITIES:

A.
1. Introduce the importance of being able to identify leisure interests, either past or present. Generate a list of interests within the group.
2. Discuss the availability of these resources within the participants' communities.
3. Provide the group with telephone books and relevant literature in the center of the table. With the group seated at tables, distribute one handout to each person.
4. Participants are instructed to complete the sheet with the names and phone numbers of where it is possible to participate in the different activities.
5. Draw participants' attention to the "special interests" location on the *hunt*. This location is for an interest that is not already listed on the sheet. Encourage the participants to complete this spot with a special interest.
6. When the *hunt* is completed, the participants can share the information that was gathered. Encourage the participants to share the "special interest" location on the *hunt*.
7. At the end of the *hunt,* take time to share resources or ideas that could have been overlooked.
8. Process by discussing how easy or difficult it was to complete the different sections on the *hunt,* what group members found out about the community that was not known before, and what resources on the table were most helpful.

B. For this activity access to transportation is necessary.
1. Introduce the importance of being able to develop leisure interests, either past or present. Generate a list of leisure interests within the group.
2. Discuss the availability of these resources within the participants communities.
3. Divide the group into teams and distribute a treasure hunt sheet to each team. Prepare the teams to go on an outing.
4. Instruct participants to complete the sheet with the names and phone numbers of where to participate, along with some literature from that place. This information is secured by visiting the specific facility or agency. Divide up the list as needed to accommodate time constraints.
5. Draw participants' attention to the "special interests" location on the *hunt*. This location is for an interest that is not already listed on the sheet. Encourage the participants to complete this spot with a special interest.
6. After the *hunt* is completed (either following this session or in the next session) encourage the participants to share the information that was gathered.
7. Develop a resource notebook from the literature gathered for all participants to use.
8. Process activity by asking group members what was learned about each one's community and to identify two constructive ways to use free-time in the future.

Activity handout and facilitator's information adapted from submission by
Lori Rosenberg, MS, CTRS, RTCR, University Heights, OH.

M	T	W	Th	F	S	S
W	**E**	**E**	**K**	**E**	**N**	**D**

Planning

Step 1: Evaluate your use of free-time. Write ways you use your free-time...the healthy ways and the unhealthy ways. Draw a line through the triangle to make a see-saw, to see how your healthy and unhealthy ways 'stack up'.

HEALTHY WAYS		UNHEALTHY WAYS
7. ________________		________________.7
6. ________________		________________.6
5. ________________		________________.5
4. ________________		________________.4
3. ________________		________________.3
2. ________________		________________.2
1. ________________		________________.1
↑ Start Here		Start Here ↑

Step 2: Plan your weekends by making healthy choices.

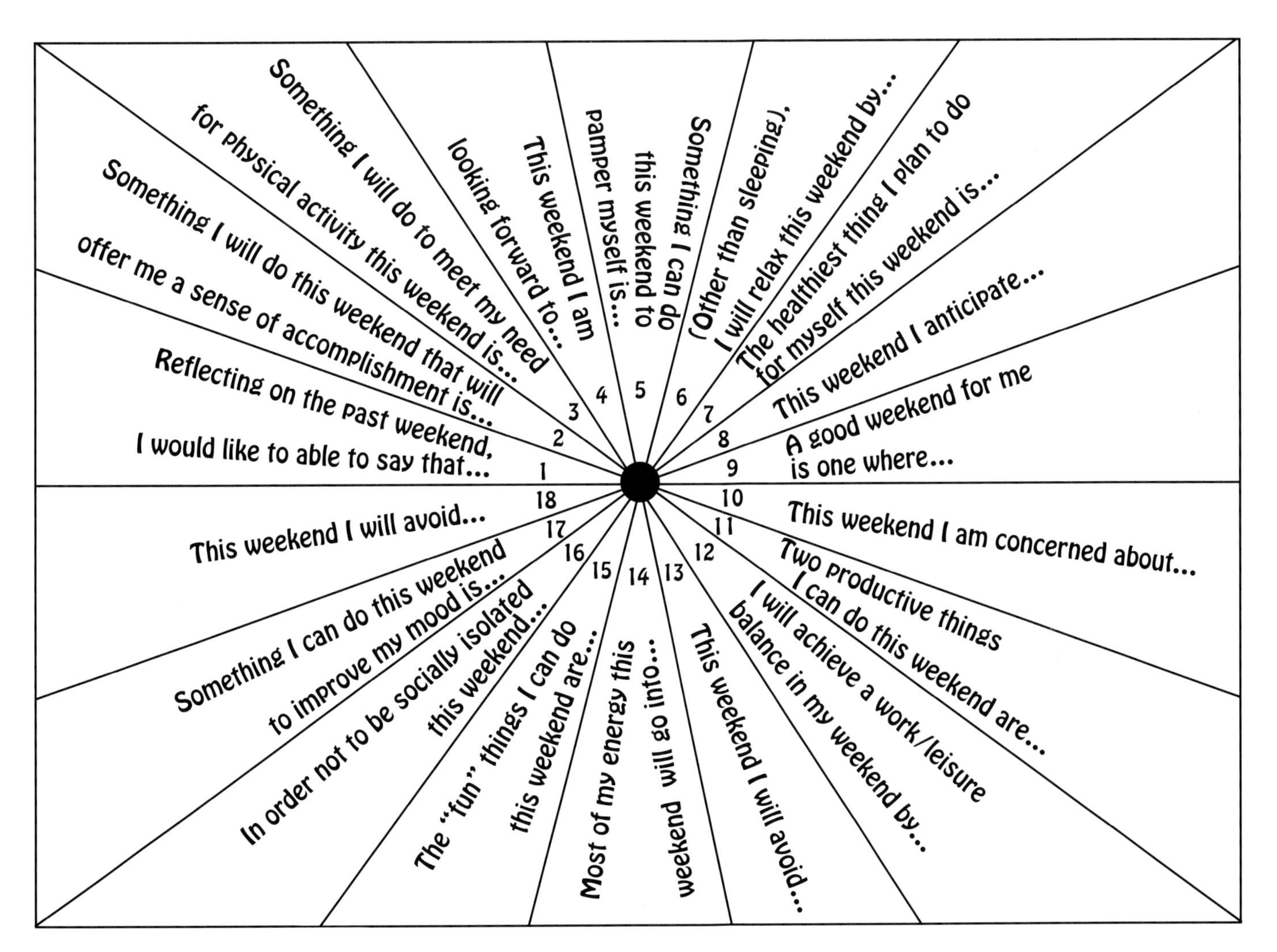

WEEKEND Planning

I. PURPOSE:

To increase leisure involvements by:
1) evaluating use of free-time, and
2) planning healthy weekends.

II. GENERAL COMMENTS:

People use free-time in ways that are healthy and unhealthy. Sometimes, evaluating use of time reveals a lack of time management habits and leisure involvements. It can be helpful to anticipate what upcoming weekends will look like in an effort to effectively plan them. Some people might have positive experiences from the past to draw upon, whereas others might only have negative ones. Planning weekends might be especially challenging (and effective) for people who have been in treatment and accustomed to the structure of daily treatment groups. In acknowledging such, people are encouraged to take responsibility and to independently plan and manage time in a healthy way.

III. POSSIBLE ACTIVITIES:

A. 1. Distribute handouts and explain as outlined in PURPOSE and GENERAL COMMENTS.

2. Instruct group members to complete Step 1. Discuss by asking group members: "Were there more healthy or unhealthy activities?" "Can leisure activities be added to the healthy side?" Brainstorm additional leisure activities to supplement sparse lists.

3. Develop a game by putting a spinner (use three dice and follow total number if unable to find or create a spinner) in the center of the circle in Step 2.

4. Ask each group member to take several turns answering incomplete sentences.

5. Process by asking group members to set realistic goals for the upcoming weekend.

B. 1. Ask group members to list those qualities that would accompany a "successful weekend". Discuss.

2. Distribute handout and explain that sometimes unhealthy patterns turn into habits. Use the following example: *Although TV watching can be relaxing for a couple of hours, it can be an unhealthy activity for an entire day.* Ask group members to complete Step 1.

3. Evaluate group responses comparing similarities and differences.

4. Divide group into two to three subgroups for Step 2.

5. Explain to the subgroups that each group member must complete the same number of incomplete sentences as there were total of ways of using free-time from Step 1., e.g., if a group member had four unhealthy ways and two healthy ways , then s/he will answer six incomplete sentences.

6. Reconvene as a larger group. Process by asking each group member to identify the question that was most thought provoking and might provide the most help or insight for the future.

Activity handout and facilitator's information adapted from respective submissions by
Jennifer E. Laabs, CTRS, Aberdeen, SD and Maggie Moriarty, M.Ed, COTA/L, Bloomfield, CT.

THE

'S of RAISING RESPONSIBLE CHILDREN

HELPING YOUR CHILD TO BECOME RESPONSIBLE

Responsible children try to be... helpful to others, kind, sympathetic, friendly, truthful, considerate and respectful of the rules of fair play with regard to friends, family, neighbors and those at school.

Effective parents teach children the difference between right and wrong, good and bad, safe and dangerous. Children learn that their behaviors, whether good or bad, produce consequences. If they are good, then good things usually happen. If they are bad, then bad things usually happen.

What influences our childrens' ability to be responsible? Here are a few factors:

ctions of adults - *By observing the actions and words of adults (parents, teachers, clergy, scout leaders, sports heroes, performers, etc.) children learn either the right or wrong way to behave. Role modeling is a very powerful tool. Parents have an especially important role here. Children will often imitate the words and actions of their parents.*

eing labeled - *There are positive and negative labels. An example of a negative label is if the Mom says, "You're a bad boy. Mason, you're always hitting your sister!" Mom would not label if instead she said, "Mason, what you're doing is hurting your sister. I love you both and I don't want anyone to get hurt. Come over here, Mason, and we'll wash the dishes together." Positive labels increase self-esteem and risk-taking abilities, e.g., "Mason, I can always count on you to be a big helper!"*

onsequences of behavior - *For every action, there is a reaction. For example: Every time Arielle shares her new toy with her sister, Mom and Dad smile and would be more likely to give her a new responsibility. But when Arielle is selfish or breaks her sister's games, Mom or Dad must talk to her again about not being selfish and respecting the rights of others. Arielle can learn about responsibility in both scenarios.*

eveloping a value system - *By learning a value system where rules are taught and clearly understood, ethical standards are formed. These become part of the very nature or conscience of a child. Secure children rely on their value system for choosing acceptable circumstances, friends, behavior, judgements and goals.*

Here is a list of possible interactions with children. Write the letter A, B, C or D that corresponds with the possible interaction. (More than one letter may be used.)

_____ praising a child for an unselfish act
_____ saying "If you forget your packed lunch, you'll need to buy it at school."
_____ complimenting your child
_____ saying "You're stupid!"
_____ taking a child on an excursion for "alone time" when you are especially pleased
_____ saying "You're so clever."
_____ explaining that "There is no swearing in this household."
_____ saying "We are so proud of you today."
_____ returning a $10.00 bill to the rightful owner in a store
_____ saying "I like the way you gave your brother a ride. You can borrow the car Saturday night."
_____ giving children weekly jobs
_____ saying "We were glad we could count on you today for walking the dog. Thank you."

THE ABCD'S of RAISING RESPONSIBLE CHILDREN

I. PURPOSE:

To increase awareness of some factors that influences a child's ability to become responsible.

II. GENERAL COMMENTS:

One of the best foundations for teaching responsibility to children is the commitment of parents/caregivers to foster responsibility. A loving approach helps children want to do "more" and accept their parents/caregivers as role models. Children watch the actions of adults very carefully to learn how to behave. Negative labels lower a child's self-image and discourage responsibility. Positive labels foster self-image and offer heights children desire. Consequences are the results of taking or not taking responsibility. Instilling a value system will shape how children will view responsibility their entire lives. This list of four factors that influence a child's ability to become responsible is not meant to be exhaustive, but instead a "start" in the world of teaching responsibility.

III. POSSIBLE ACTIVITIES:

A. 1. Distribute handouts and explain topic using above stated PURPOSE and GENERAL COMMENTS.

2. Read together as a group and complete the bottom section together.
3. Brainstorm examples of each of the four factors:
   a. actions of adults
   b. being labeled
   c. consequences of behavior
   d. developing a value system
4. Ask each group member to set four goals that could be implemented to assist a child in becoming more responsible, e.g., "I will point out to my child the various responsibilities I take." "I will use positive labels daily with each of my children." "I will offer positive consequences to Arielle when she keeps her room clean for 1 week." "I will make my concerns known regarding swearing in the house."
5. Discuss as a group each other's goals.
6. Process benefits of becoming aware of what influences a child's ability to become responsible.

B. 1. Discuss the importance of children becoming responsible and the parent/caregiver role.

2. Distribute handouts explaining that there are a lot of factors that affect a child's ability to become responsible, but this discussion will be limited to the outlined four factors.
3. Ask group members to complete handout independently after reading top section together. Share as a group.
4. Discuss the following paragraphs:

   Being responsible can be a difficult path for some children. Some want to find the easy route, the fastest way and/or the least difficult task. Some do not mind stepping on others' toes, telling lies, forgetting tasks and hurting themselves and others.

   Parents who whip, hit, scream, lecture, argue, tease, taunt, humiliate or intimidate children into becoming responsible are losing in many ways.

   Teaching rules, enforcing rules and being a good role model are the best ways for helping children become responsible. If children are surrounded by responsible people, they will often (not always) become responsible too.
5. Emphasize the importance of increasing children's ability to accept responsibility. Process by discussing ways of how to incorporate ideas shared in this group into personal lives.

Activity handout and facilitator's information adapted from submission by
John F. Murphy, M.Ed. and Ann M. Murphy, M.Ed., Hingham, MA.

Effective Discipline

Discipline begins with love.
It is important to show love by smiles, hugs & kisses, listening and kind supportive words. Only after a loving environment is established can effective discipline take place.

1..2..3..4..5..6..7..

Here are 5 steps for effective disciplining:

1. **Be in control when you are disciplining.** If you are angry, screaming, yelling and/or hitting...this is not the time to discipline your child.

   List 3 ways you can get in control.
   1. ______________________________
   2. ______________________________
   3. ______________________________

2. **Make rules.** Have rules for safety, for getting along with people, for manners and other things that you consider important for your child's growth and well-being. Remember, however, too many rules only confuse children and make them feel guilty, so keep rules to a minimum.

   What is one new rule you are considering for your children?

   ____

   Why is this rule important to you and your family?

   ____

3. **Make sure your children understand the rules.** Rules need to be clearly taught. Some children disobey because they do not understand the rules.

   How can you explain the new rule in a way that your child(ren) will surely understand?

   ____

4. **Be okay with saying "NO".** You cannot always be popular with your children. At times you must say clearly and firmly "NO" and stick with it! Parents must show their rightful authority over children if youngsters are going to learn right from wrong, good from bad, and safety from danger.

   Give an example of when you were told "NO" as a child and if it was in your best interest.

   ____

   Give an example of a tough situation you've been in lately where it's been difficult to say "NO" to your child(ren).

   ____

5. **Be prepared to be an enforcer.** To enforce rules when unacceptable behavior occurs, "time-out" for young children is effective (one minute for each year of life). Depriving older children of TV time or going out with friends serves the same purpose. This is much more effective than yelling, screaming, hitting, insulting, etc. A quiet talk, after the upsetting incident is much better than all the yelling in the world – for both sides!

   List 2 effective time-outs for each child.
   1. ______________________________
   2. ______________________________

Love and Limits = Effective Discipline

I. PURPOSE:

To teach parents/caregivers that discipline begins with love and continues with consistency, good rules and the enforcement of rules.

II. GENERAL COMMENTS:

Effective discipline requires parents/caregivers to teach rules before they punish. It requires love, patience and understanding. It includes consistency, firmness and kindness. For many parents and caregivers, the role of an effective disciplinarian is especially challenging, because it is not familiar from the past. Most people who were raised in a home with insulting words, yelling and hitting realize the damage done and want to avoid this at all costs.

III. POSSIBLE ACTIVITIES:

A. 1. Distribute handouts and ask each group member to complete.

2. Discuss as a group, emphasizing that it is important to offer each other support, understanding and kindness.

3. Facilitate discussion of each of the five steps for effective discipline with these "starters".

a. *"I hit him and yelled at him and I threw him out of the house . . . and he just got worse."* The dad believed that the best way to discipline was to get more and more angry and then children will somehow get better. What could the consequences be to the child? To the dad?

b. A caregiver said, *"I try to find time when I'm not angry or upset . . . then I sit down with my children and explain to them the do's and do not's of our family living. I teach them my rules."* The caregiver even tried to let the children give input, too, so that they'd have a say in the rules. How would children respond to this approach?

c. A child (age 7) is consistently late, despite reminders to be home at 5:30. What question(s) would you need to ask the child to see if s/he understood the rule?

d. Is there a point that there are too many "no's"? Is there a need to prioritize? *"No, you can not play in the woods or on the city streets!" "No, you can not stay up past your bedtime." "No, you can not go to a party where there will be drinking and drugs or no adult supervision."* Discuss that "NO" at times is part of being a good parent, and it is a word of love. *"I love you so much, I CAN say NO to you."*

e. Overlook occasional slip-ups of children. They will appreciate this. These are the little things that happen in the course of the day that don't need to be a big deal, e.g., the spilled milk, the wet pants, the swear word, the poor mark in school, the forgotten house key, etc. Why is it good to overlook the occasional slip-up? What other slip-ups could be added to this list? We, as adults would appreciate if people did not scold our every little mistake and children appreciate this, too. Discuss that this is not being a permissive parent, rather it is being a human parent who has compassion and not a need to yell at every little thing.

4. Process benefits of effective disciplining.

B. 1. Introduce topic by explaining above stated PURPOSE and GENERAL COMMENTS.

2. Distribute handouts, review and give group members ten minutes to complete.

3. Divide group into pairs to share answers.

4. Give each pair the assignment of describing the benefits of effective discipline for children and the parent/caregivers as well.

5. Allow each pair to share and discuss commonalities.

6. Facilitate discussion about community resources available to support effective discipline for parents and caregivers.

Activity handout and facilitator's information adapted from submission by
John F. Murphy, M.Ed., and Ann M. Murphy, M.Ed., Hingham, MA.

IS LOVE IN YOUR HOME?

One of the most important parts of parenting is showing love to our children! From the time they are babies, through their elementary school days, high school years, and yes, even into adulthood, they need our love and encouragement. They need to hear us say, "You're wonderful! I love you!"

Smiles	*Hugs & Kisses*	*Listening*	*Kind supportive words*
Your *smile* shows your love. How many times do you *smile* at, or with, your child in 1 day? ______ Are smiles part of your daily routine? ____ Do you smile more than you frown? ________________ ________________	Your *hugs & kisses* show love. Sometimes we need the most love when we are the least lovable. How many times do you usually hug and kiss your child on an average day? ______When do you kiss and hug your child?______________	*Listening* shows love to children... without watching TV, reading, talking on the phone or gazing out the window. How often do you really listen to your child each day?______________ ________________ ________________	The *words* parents say to their children are vital communication links. Words can either bind parent-child relationship closely together or they can tear them apart. Words can be a determining factor in the harmony or lack of harmony in the home environment. How many times do you praise your child in a typical day? ______

Other special ways of showing love...

NOTES from parents/caregivers let children know in a concrete way that they have their support and love. Youngsters often keep these written treasures to read again in times of stress.

PATIENCE from parents/caregivers let children know that they love them. Take time to cool off before reacting.

What are some other special ways you can think of that shows parental love?

1. ____
2. ____
3. ____

Someone once said *"As soon as I walk into a house, I get the feeling of a family. I look at their faces to see if they are smiling at one another. I listen to what they say, hoping I will hear words of praise, not put-downs. I watch to see how they move about and interact with another. If love is in this home, I feel good. If I do not sense this accepting and understanding of family members, I want to get out as soon as possible."*

How would that person feel, walking into YOUR home? ____________________

IS LOVE IN YOUR HOME?

I. PURPOSE:

To identify and practice skills which bring a more loving atmosphere into the home.

II. GENERAL COMMENTS:

Effective parenting means raising children in a loving, caring environment. Parents/caregivers who give children an abundance of approval and support are providing an enriching atmosphere for a happy home life. Love must be *shown*, not *assumed*. While having firm expectations and good rules for discipline, one can replace overly critical and negative practices with words and actions of care, love and trust.

III. POSSIBLE ACTIVITIES:

A. 1. Distribute handouts and ask group members to complete.

2. Discuss the questions under "SMILES", concluding with the fact that smiles say to a child "I love you", "I'm proud of you", and "I'm on your side!".

3. Discuss the questions under "HUGS AND KISSES", brainstorming the time that kids can best use hugs and kisses, i.e., good morning hugs, good night hugs and kisses, congratulations hugs, hugs for no reason at all, etc. Mention that with babies, parents/caregivers hug and kiss quite naturally, but as children enter elementary, middle and high school, often the hugs from parents/caregivers disappear. Children need this kind of indication of love throughout ALL their years, even into adulthood.

4. Ask group to brainstorm tips on good listening to children, i.e.,

Don't let your mind wander.
Try to relax.
Don't prejudge, just listen.
Don't think about your response while child is talking.
Be interested in what they are saying, even if you must pretend.
Don't interrupt.
Don't make fun of what they're saying, or the way they say it.
Let your whole body listen (eye-to-eye contact, nod of head, etc.)

5. Discuss that kind supportive words show love to children. If words are kind, they are okay. If they are not kind, they are not okay. Sarcasm, ridicule, yelling, swearing or screaming do NOT show love. Present the question "What are some kind supportive words that could be said to children, even when the parent/caregiver is not feeling positive?", i.e., "That's an interesting point of view. I hadn't thought of it in that way, however ...", "Well, that's a mature approach to take.", "I like the way you're communicating on a touchy subject!", etc.

6. Process the activity by brainstorming the benefits to a child when there is love in a home.

B. 1. Distribute handouts and ask group members to complete.

2. Ask each group member to flip page and to write a description of a family in a happy home situation. Make sure that group members know the family dynamics well enough to comment with details about what constitutes a happy home. It can be from the group member's own family, a friend or relative's family, a family from a book, from a television sitcom, etc.

3. Ask group members to write the four topics from the front of the handout (SMILES, HUGS AND KISSES, LISTENING and KIND SUPPORTIVE WORDS) and to recall how those parent/caregivers interacted.

4. Instruct group members to list any other observations of other signs of love in this family that were noticed.

5. Ask volunteers to read paper to the group.

6. Process activity by discussing commonalities of chosen families and ways of bringing a more loving atmosphere in the home.

Activity handout and facilitator's information adapted from submission by
John F. Murphy, M.Ed., and Ann M. Murphy, M.Ed., Hingham, MA.

Deepening Relationships

Dear ______________________________,

I am writing to you to share what has been going on for me this ________________.
(week, month, etc.)

EMOTIONALLY

I felt __________________ when _______________________________________.
(emotion) (describe event and circumstances surrounding it)

I felt __________________ when _______________________________________.
(emotion) (describe event and circumstances surrounding it)

I felt __________________ when _______________________________________.
(emotion) (describe event and circumstances surrounding it)

PHYSICALLY (Describe how you felt: did you exercise, sleep well, injure yourself, etc.?)

MENTALLY (Describe what you thought significantly about and how often)

SPIRITUALLY (Describe your recent relations with a power greater than yourself)

PROFESSIONALLY (Describe what has been challenging and/or fulfilling you at school or work as well as your current hopes or desires in that area)

ABOUT FAMILY (Describe how you have related to, or thought about, members of your family)

ABOUT US (Describe how you have related to, thought about, and felt in regards to this person. Cite one quality you love and appreciate about this individual. If you feel a need to improve an aspect of your relationship, cite specifically what you will do to foster such improvement and then specifically what you would like the other person to consider doing).

Thank you for taking the time to learn more about me!

Deepening Relationships

I. PURPOSE:

To deepen communication between two individuals.

To heighten awareness of one's self and others.

To examine holistic functioning over a given period of time.

II. GENERAL COMMENTS:

Many relationships develop a predictable pattern of communication. Such patterns may enable stagnation within the relationship or limit the depth at which individuals may know and function with one another. Using writing (rather than talking) which is focused on self-exploration leads to revelations which stimulate and support deeper and more meaningful relationships.

III. POSSIBLE ACTIVITIES:

A. 1. Discuss the concept that successful relationships require energy, time and excellent communication.

2. Distribute handouts and ask individuals to write to a significant other, not necessarily in this group, as honestly and completely as able. Give approximately ten minutes.

3. Divide group into pairs, instructing each person to read to partner and vice versa, encouraging supportive listening without verbal feedback.

4. Ask individuals:
   Which parts of the letter would be beneficial to share with significant others?
   What would be the potential benefits?
   What could be the negative consequences?
   When is a good time to share?
   Would there be value in writing and not sharing immediately?
   Would there be value in writing and not sharing at all?

5. Process by asking what was learned from this group session.

B. 1. Divide group into pairs.

2. Distribute handouts. Instruct each group member to complete the letter, addressing it to their partner. Use the past week as the given period of time.

3. Explain that when the two exchange letters, each must read the letter TWO times before saying anything. The appropriate initial response after reading the letter is to be, "Thank you for writing to me". This may be followed by any specific comments or questions either reader may have.

4. Facilitate a discussion among group members about the ease or difficulty of this task. Question how well partners know each other in a holistic manner. Ask how this activity may improve group relations.

5. Suggest that group members and/or their significant others set up an ongoing schedule within which to write and exchange such letters.

Activity handout and facilitator's information adapted from submission by Terri Marshall-Schrader, M.Ed., Helotes, TX.

DEVELOPING boundaries

People with healthy boundaries...
Check off boxes that apply to you.

- ☐ have limits and recognize what they are
- ☐ know what they will or will not do
- ☐ know what they will allow others to do, not do

People with unhealthy boundaries...
Check off boxes that apply to you.

- ☐ don‘t know what information to share
- ☐ allow others to hurt them
- ☐ don’t easily trust
- ☐ trust too easily
- ☐ trust untrustworthy people
- ☐ don‘t trust trust-worthy people
- ☐ have poorly defined limits
- ☐ don’t know what information to share with others
- ☐ are overly tolerant of inappropriate behaviors
- ☐ are very intolerant of inappropriate behaviors

At times, we all have healthy and unhealthy boundaries and as we grow and change, it is OK to adapt, move and adjust our limits. People in our lives need to know that we have boundaries and what they are. These boundaries help them and us . . . and help relationships in general!

Take a few minutes to review who is in your circle of support.
Write your name in the rectangle. Identify supportive people in your life by writing the names of supportive people on the circle according to how much they are trusted. Close to the person indicates more trust and further away indicates less trust.

What limits do you need to establish with those closest to you?

____

____

What limits do you need to establish with those distant from you?

____

____

DEVELOPING boundaries

I. PURPOSE:

To improve relationships by understanding and developing healthy boundaries.

II. GENERAL COMMENTS:

Developing healthy boundaries can be a crucial step in both healthy relationships and in stress management. For many, the concept of boundaries may be a new one. Several areas need to be explored when discussing boundaries such as, trust issues, level of personal disclosures, tolerance and acceptance of others' behaviors, and expectations of others and ourselves. Analyzing the types of relationships one is in presently, and deciding what limits need to be established, can be challenging as well as empowering.

III. POSSIBLE ACTIVITIES:

A. 1. Distribute handouts and read top section with the group. Offer a continuum concept of loose, medium and rigid boundaries if helpful.

2. List on flip chart the "Benefits of Boundaries", e.g., knowing where you stand, knowing what to expect, security, safety.

3. Review bottom section of handout and give group members 5-10 minutes to complete.

4. Share as a group the limits that need to be established.

5. Process by reviewing the characteristics of people with healthy and unhealthy boundaries and ask each group member to state one benefit of establishing limits.

B. 1. Using a flip chart, write the words "developing boundaries" and underneath record what the group understands and perceives of these words. Offer additional information as needed.

2. Ask group members to consider what the world would be like with no boundaries and brainstorm, e.g., not knowing what the weather would be like tomorrow, not knowing speed limits, not knowing criminal laws, etc.

3. Distribute handouts and ask group members to complete.

4. Share group responses and discuss commonalities and differences.

5. Process by asking group members how developing boundaries relate to healthy relationships and stress management.

Activity handout and facilitator's information adapted from submission by Sharen Bowen, R.P.N., Ottawa, ON.

SUPPORTIVE relationships

It is wise to trust "supportive people".

SUPPORTIVE PEOPLE...

- keep us from feeling alone
- offer approval
- are honest
-
- give strength
- want what is "best for us"
- help us to keep our heads up
-
- supply us with kind listening
- keep us from falling or sinking
- speak in favor of us
-

What would a supportive person say to you? ______________________

What would a supportive person do for you? ______________________

What would a supportive person do with you?______________________

Knowing what information to share and when to share is a healthy boundary, and will assist in developing supportive relationships.

What does "private" mean to you? ______________________

Why do people need to keep some thoughts to themselves sometimes? ______________________

What happens to you if you tell everyone everything all the time?______________________

How does that affect the way people treat you? ______________________

What type of information do you feel comfortable sharing? ______________________

Who are you most comfortable sharing private information with?______________________

❶ Here's a list of "difficult situations". Circle one that you might have been up against recently or might be up against in the near future:

- financial problems
- significant other/ marital concerns
- feeling sick
- unwanted pregnancy
- religious/spiritual conflicts
- family problems
- feelings of fear

❷ Write the name of the person, in the center rectangle, with whom you'd share this information. ❸ Write on the inside of the square what you would feel comfortable sharing. ❹ Write on the outside of the square the type of information you'd feel uncomfortable sharing.

SUPPORTIVE relationships

I. PURPOSE:

To improve supportive relationships by:
1) recognizing qualities of supportive people
2) establishing boundaries using discriminating levels of personal disclosures.

II. GENERAL COMMENTS:

Supportive relationships can be very powerful for everyone, and especially those who are in the recovery process. Trust issues and the level of personal disclosures are two common themes often discussed when people are looking to (or being encouraged to) enlarge their circle of support.

III. POSSIBLE ACTIVITIES: This handout can be used in conjunction with NO ONE IS AN Is-LAND (page 43), Life Management Skills I.

A. 1. Distribute handouts.

2. Read together list of qualities of supportive people. Ask each group member to add to the printed list. Offer physical examples of support, e.g., four legs for a table or trusses for a bridge demonstrating with blocks or books for further reinforcement.
3. Instruct group members to complete the questions following the list and discuss.
4. Explain to the group that supportive relationships are based on healthy boundaries. Read questions aloud to the group, offering examples as needed.
5. Give group ten minutes to complete the six questions.
6. Discuss as a group, reinforcing need for boundaries.
7. Instruct group members to complete "Here's a list..." section.
8. Process by asking group members, "What is the importance of establishing supportive relationships and what steps are needed to accomplish this?"

B. 1. Distribute handouts and ask group members to complete, clarifying as needed.

2. Focus on the development of establishing boundaries by role-playing specific situations from group members' handouts. For example, if a group member indicated that 'financial problems' was a 'difficult situation', then ask two to three group members to role-play significant members in that person's life (nosy neighbor, meddling mother, interested in-law).
3. Encourage group members to offer support and feedback.
4. Involve everyone in the group before instructing group members to complete last question.
5. Process by asking group members what each learned from this activity.

Activity handout and facilitator's information adapted from submission by Sharen Bowen, R.P.N., Ottawa, ON.

Savvy Socializing

Before making a major purchase, a wise consumer needs information, techniques and education. The same applies to finding a healthy and satisfying emotional relationship.

Asking a potential partner to answer some questions is okay but WHAT can you ask and WHEN do you ask them?

IMPORTANT QUALITIES — **TIMING (check when appropriate)**

List qualities you are looking for in a potential partner.

	Before 1st date	On 1st date	Later	Never
Example a) *Goals & ambitions*	✔			
Example b) *Honesty in relationships*		✔		
1)				
2)				
3)				
4)				
5)				
6)				
7)				
8)				

THESE ARE ISSUES TO BE EXPLORED

Write open-ended, non-threatening questions / statements about the qualities you listed above that you can ask in a caring, attentive and friendly way.

Example a) *Where do you see yourself 5 years from now?*

Example b) *Tell me about your last relationship.*

1) ______
2) ______
3) ______
4) ______
5) ______
6) ______
7) ______
8) ______

FOR FURTHER INVESTIGATION

How can you go about finding a potential partner with the qualities listed above?

Example a) *Goals & ambitions: discussion groups, classes.*

Example b) *Honesty: church / temple groups, volunteering.*

1) ______
2) ______
3) ______
4) ______
5) ______
6) ______
7) ______
8) ______

Savvy Socializing

I. PURPOSE:

To recognize qualities important to healthy personal relationships.

To identify constructive ways of finding healthy personal relationships.

II. GENERAL COMMENTS:

Even those who are experienced daters often tend to suspend sound judgment and rational thinking when it comes to relationships. Desire alone for a relationship does not make it work. A healthy relationship requires self-awareness, insight, the ability to ask questions and energy.

III. POSSIBLE ACTIVITIES:

A. 1. Acquire a copy of singles ads from the classified sections of newspapers. Photocopy both men and women's ads, making enough copies for every member of the group.

2. Distribute copies of the singles ads. Ask group members to review, noting qualities listed. Write listed qualities on chalkboard.

3. Distribute handouts. Ask individuals to imagine what each one's ad would include. Instruct group members to complete top section. Refer to Life Management Skills III, CHARACTERISTICS OF A HEALTHY RELATIONSHIP, page 31, if needed. Lead a discussion on importance of asking questions.

4. Discuss difference between an open and closed-ended question. Instruct group members to complete middle of handout.

5. Give a 3" x 5" card to each group member. Instruct group members to write one question/statement on the card from the middle section of the handout. Collect cards and place in a basket.

6. Instruct one person at a time to select a card from the basket, read the question aloud, and if it is an open-ended question, to answer it appropriately. If question is closed-ended, assist group members to rewrite it as open-ended and instruct same person to answer.

7. Ask group members to complete bottom third of handout. Brainstorm additional locations / opportunities where one might meet a potential partner with the listed qualities.

B. 1. Distribute handouts and ask group to complete top third of handout.

2. Ask group members to self-disclose one quality each is looking for in a potential partner, listing them on the chalkboard.

3. Introduce topic of open and closed-ended questions. Using qualities listed on the board, assist group members to develop open-ended questions for each.

4. Ask group to fill in the "These are Issues to be Explored" section of the handout, creating questions applicable to each person's listed qualities.

5. Instruct members to complete the "For Further Investigation" section.

6. Ask each group member to share one important quality, the open-ended question or statement, and a way of finding this potential partner. Elicit assistance from the group for additional ideas of ways that person might find a partner.

7. Process activity by discussing the benefits of actively looking for valued qualities in a potential partner.

Activity handout and facilitator's information adapted from submission by Elaine M. Hyla, M.Ed., Euclid, OH.

Life Choices... Baby Time - or Not!

Whether or not to have a baby is an important choice!
When making this choice many factors need to be responsibly considered.
To help you decide whether or not this is the right time for you to become a parent, you need to look carefully at why you would choose to have a baby.

Make a check (✓) beside each statement
that you feel is a good reason for you to choose to have a baby at this time.

- ☐ I'll have a companion
- ☐ I love children
- ☐ I want something new
- ☐ It would make my partner happy
- ☐ I want a child despite the fact that I'm unmarried
- ☐ I want to start my own family
- ☐ I'm lonely
- ☐ My biological clock is ticking
- ☐ It's expected of me
- ☐ It'll keep my relationship together
- ☐ I'm ready
- ☐ I'll have someone of my very own
- ☐ I don't want to be alone anymore
- ☐ I want unconditional love
- ☐ I feel peer and/or family pressure
- ☐ Everyone else has one
- ☐ To ensure a future family name
- ☐ I want to complete my relationship
- ☐ I'll have someone to care for me later
- ☐ I like getting attention
- ☐ ______________________________
- ☐ ______________________________
- ☐ It will help me to grow personally
- ☐ It would be good for my significant other
- ☐ I don't have other plans for the future
- ☐ I wouldn't have to give up my schooling
- ☐ I wouldn't have to give up my career
- ☐ I just feel like it
- ☐ I am ready to give up some personal time
- ☐ I can handle more responsibility
- ☐ I'd like to be a young parent
- ☐ I can afford it
- ☐ My partner wants to have a baby
- ☐ It'll help me to be more flexible
- ☐ I'm ready to make a commitment
- ☐ I feel secure in my relationship
- ☐ This is good timing for me
- ☐ I can give a child everything it needs
- ☐ I feel able to handle the stress
- ☐ I'd be a good role model
- ☐ It's OK to give up some of my independence
- ☐ I have always had a desire to have children
- ☐ ______________________________
- ☐ ______________________________

List your 3 most important statements:

1. ____
2. ____
3. ____

As you review the above statements, do you feel you are making a good choice at this time?

Yes ☐ No ☐

Why? / Why not? ____

____

Life Choices ... Baby Time - or Not!

I. PURPOSE:

To promote responsibility by using critical thinking and a self-questioning method regarding the choice of becoming a parent.

II. GENERAL COMMENTS:

It is often thought that having a baby is a given right. This is not true. Becoming a parent is a responsibility and an important choice. There are many reasons individuals choose to have a baby. Understanding the emotions behind such choices aids one in determining if this is the right time and the right reasons for making such an important choice.

Life choices such as having a baby are emotional and value driven. This handout should be used by trained facilitators. Personal values and beliefs need to be carefully monitored.

III. POSSIBLE ACTIVITIES:

A. 1. Distribute handouts and ask each participant to complete all but the last question.
   2. List every participant's three most important statements on a flip chart or chalkboard.
   3. Ask each participant to discuss their three most important statements.
   4. Encourage discussion among the group.
   5. Ask participants to complete the remaining question.
   6. Encourage participants to share their final answer with the group.
   7. Process the activity by discussing the many factors involved in making this important choice.
   8. For further exploration, distribute a second handout, asking participants to complete as if it were a decision to be made three or six months from now.

B. 1. Discuss what it means to be a parent.
   2. Distribute handouts. Use it as a resource to promote discussion.
   3. Discuss each statement as a "right" or "wrong" reason to have a baby, encouraging an open, accepting discussion.
   4. Ask group members to narrow statements down to the strongest, most supportive three to five statements of why each would choose to have a baby.
   5. Instruct group members to complete the final question and state how they feel about their choice.
   6. Process by discussing the implications to both parent and child of making the best possible choice.

Sandra Negley, MTRS, CTRS, Salt Lake City, UT, edited front of handout and submitted facilitator's information.

What's your Excuse?

Bills overdue? Missed the deadline on the project? Sending belated birthday cards this year? Stood up your date Saturday night? Showed up late for the meeting? So what's your excuse . . . ?

- ☐ Something came up that had to be taken care of.
- ☐ I forgot to do it. I should have written it down.
- ☐ Do it tomorrow when I'm not feeling so weak.
- ☐ The electricity went off last night.
- ☐ A family member is hospitalized.
- ☐ A family member passed away.
- ☐ I didn't know where to look.
- ☐ Did not know what to wear.
- ☐ You were going to do that.
- ☐ Had to take out the trash.
- ☐ My house caught on fire.
- ☐ My alarm didn't go off.
- ☐ Bad hair day.
- ☐ No initiative.
- ☐ Car trouble.
- ☐ I am sick.
- ☐ Too tired.
- ☐ Forgot.
- ☐ Unexpected company.
- ☐ Basement is flooded.
- ☐ I have no babysitter.
- ☐ Had to feed the cat.
- ☐ My car broke down.
- ☐ I was in an accident.
- ☐ Going out of town.
- ☐ Have a headache.
- ☐ I have no money.
- ☐ Tied up in traffic.
- ☐ Nothing to wear.
- ☐ Procrastination.
- ☐ That's your job.
- ☐ No motivation.
- ☐ The dog ate it.

How do you put excuses to work for you . . . ? To explain why something happened? To justify your behaviors or attitudes? To place blame? To avoid unpleasant things? Recognizing that you are using excuses can be the first step toward making a change.

WHAT'S YOUR EXCUSE?

I. PURPOSE:

To increase the ability to accept responsibilities by gaining awareness of "excuse-making" patterns.

II. GENERAL COMMENTS:

Oftentimes, people have tasks that need to be done, but in reality, don't want to do. It is amazing how many excuses one can find to *get out of* a certain job/task or social situation. This exercise can help to clarify in which particular situations one looks for excuses and what kind of excuses one uses. This can be a first step toward making a very positive step in accepting responsibilities.

III. POSSIBLE ACTIVITIES:

A. 1. Distribute handouts.

2. Ask group members to review the list of excuses, checking off any that the group members have used.
3. Facilitate a discussion asking group members to tell about a time when each used an excuse. Allow group members to share common stories, agreeing and confronting each other. Humor, rather than hostility, generally facilitates this exercise.
4. Take an opportunity to bring up and discuss excuses and motivation in relationship to treatment issues, if applicable. (Some group members may have used excuses in avoiding meetings, not taking medications, not following through on prior discharge plans, not doing homemaking tasks, not seeking work, etc.)
5. Process the session by asking group members to describe their typical excuse-making pattern and how this information might be helpful in the future.

B. 1. Distribute the handout to a particular individual who has been avoiding part of the treatment program and ask him/her to complete it.

2. Meet with the client either individually or in the treatment team, to discuss why s/he has been avoiding treatment.
3. Clarify which types of excuses s/he uses so that the client and treatment team members can recognize *red flags* for avoidant behavior.
4. Write a treatment contract to identify common excuses or use the WELLNESS CONTRACT, page 58, to achieve desired goals. Consider asking team members to point out the behavior when the identified excuses appear.

Activity handout and facilitator's information adapted from submission by K. Oscar Larson, OTR, MA, Alexandria,VA.

No Place Like Home

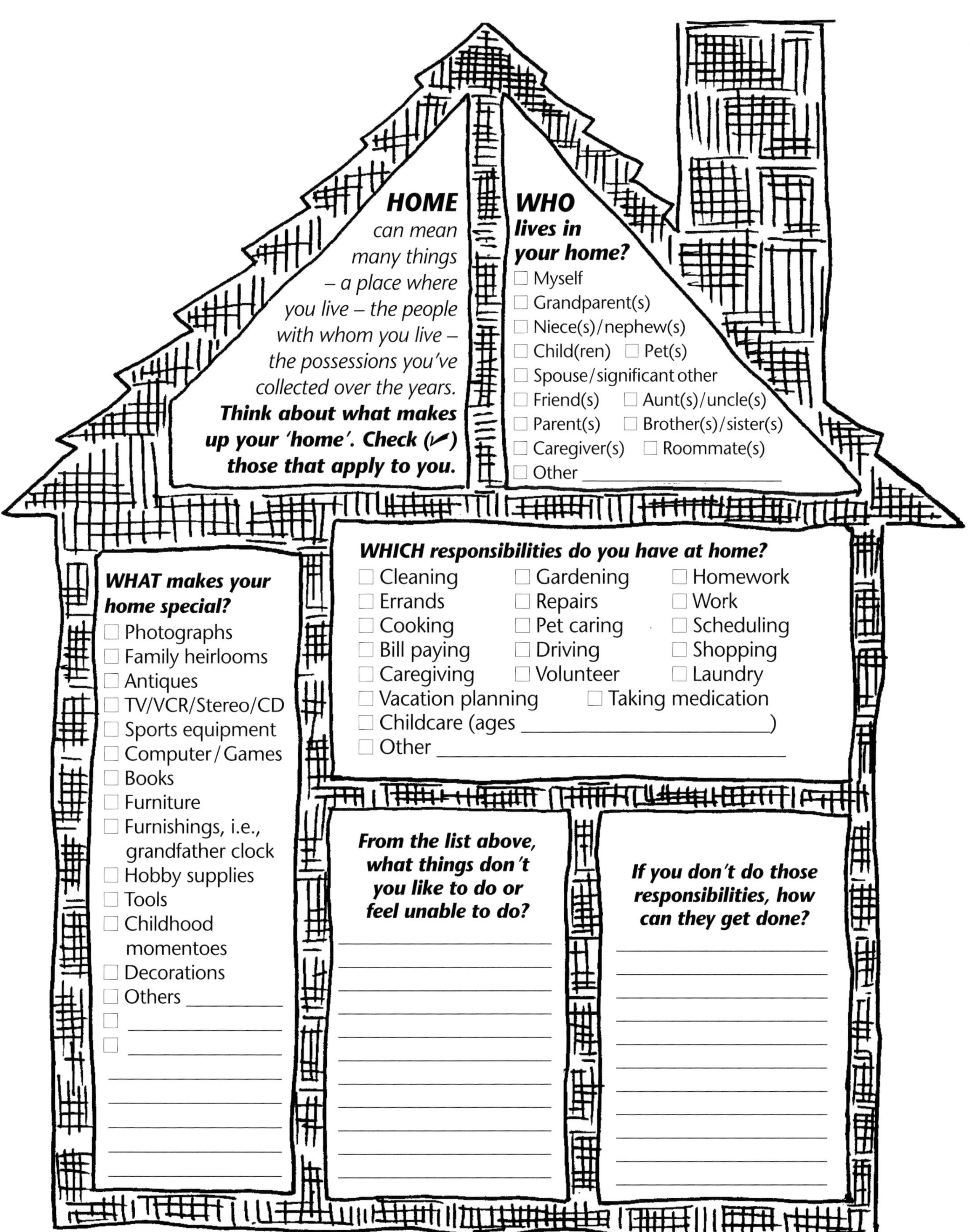

HOME *can mean many things – a place where you live – the people with whom you live – the possessions you've collected over the years.* ***Think about what makes up your 'home'. Check (✓) those that apply to you.***

WHO lives in your home?

- ☐ Myself
- ☐ Grandparent(s)
- ☐ Niece(s)/nephew(s)
- ☐ Child(ren) ☐ Pet(s)
- ☐ Spouse/significant other
- ☐ Friend(s) ☐ Aunt(s)/uncle(s)
- ☐ Parent(s) ☐ Brother(s)/sister(s)
- ☐ Caregiver(s) ☐ Roommate(s)
- ☐ Other ____________________

WHAT makes your home special?

- ☐ Photographs
- ☐ Family heirlooms
- ☐ Antiques
- ☐ TV/VCR/Stereo/CD
- ☐ Sports equipment
- ☐ Computer/Games
- ☐ Books
- ☐ Furniture
- ☐ Furnishings, i.e., grandfather clock
- ☐ Hobby supplies
- ☐ Tools
- ☐ Childhood momentoes
- ☐ Decorations
- ☐ Others __________
- ☐ ______________
- ☐ ______________

____
____
____
____
____

WHICH responsibilities do you have at home?

☐ Cleaning	☐ Gardening	☐ Homework
☐ Errands	☐ Repairs	☐ Work
☐ Cooking	☐ Pet caring	☐ Scheduling
☐ Bill paying	☐ Driving	☐ Shopping
☐ Caregiving	☐ Volunteer	☐ Laundry

- ☐ Vacation planning ☐ Taking medication
- ☐ Childcare (ages ____________________)
- ☐ Other ______________________________

From the list above, what things don't you like to do or feel unable to do?

____
____
____
____
____
____
____
____
____
____
____

If you don't do those responsibilities, how can they get done?

____
____
____
____
____
____
____
____
____
____
____

Being Responsible is the Ability to Respond to Needs

No Place Like Home

I. PURPOSE:

To identify what makes a home and which responsibilities that one has at home.

To identify which home responsibilities one may have difficulty carrying out and to assist in problem-solving ways to accomplish them.

II. GENERAL COMMENTS:

"Home" can be a castle, a ranch, a boat, an apartment, a condominium, a trailer, a room in a Skilled-care facility, a farm, etc. An ideal home is often described as a comfortable place, where a sense of order presides. This exercise identifies the "who, what and which" of a home, specifies the variety of difficult 'home' responsibilities and assists in problem solving how to complete the unpopular/difficult tasks. When one fulfills responsibilities there is a sense of accomplishment, which enhances self-esteem.

III. POSSIBLE ACTIVITIES:

A. 1. List on a chalkboard the following phrases and brainstorm their meanings with the group:

"There's no place like home"

"Man's home is his castle"

"Home sweet home"

"Home is where the heart is"

2. Distribute handouts and ask group members to complete.
3. Collect the completed handouts, shuffle and redistribute, being sure no one receives their own.
4. Instruct group members to read the other person's handout.
5. Divide group into small groups, asking individuals to compare the other person's handout and responsibilities compared to their own.
6. Instruct each group to problem solve each others "don't like to do or feel unable to do" responsibilities offering suggestions on how to accomplish them.
7. Process group by asking members to identify benefits of this activity.

B. 1. Ask each group member to name as many thoughts as possible in 15 seconds that come to mind when hearing the word "home".

2. Discuss as a group the concept of "home" and what makes where one lives *feel* like home.
3. Distribute handouts, asking each group member to complete.
4. Elicit from a volunteer their "don't like to do or feel unable to do" list and how those things can be accomplished.
5. Problem solve as a group suggestions on how these responsibilities might be completed, i.e., fun ways, organizing, delegating, asking favors (even though it might be uncomfortable), spending money to get it done, etc.
6. Continue to ask for other volunteers to disclose written lists and continue group problem solving with each.
7. Process activity by discussing how problem solving might help one to become a more responsible person and the benefits of accomplishing responsibilities at home.

Activity handout and facilitator's information adapted from submission by K. Oscar Larson, OTR, MA, Alexandria, VA.

I am someone who . . .

feels . . . thinks . . . enjoys . . . has . . . believes . . . is . . . hopes to . . . once . . . collects . . . can . . . cherishes . . . wants to . . . strives to . . . will . . . values . . . cares to . . .

1. ______________________
2. ______________________
3. ______________________
4. ______________________
5. ______________________
6. ______________________
7. ______________________
8. ______________________
9. ______________________
10. ______________________

I am someone who . . .

I. PURPOSE

To increase self-esteem by presenting oneself in a positive light.

II. GENERAL COMMENTS

The ability to acknowledge and present oneself in a positive light is a key to healthy self-esteem as well as one's ability to establish friendships. Oftentimes those who experience low self-esteem see their deficits quite readily. Our job as supportive facilitators/healthcare professionals is to help those who need to enhance self-esteem, recognize and identify their strengths and assets to compensate for possible deficits.

III. POSSIBLE ACTIVITIES

A. 1. Discuss the value in presenting oneself positively, recognizing the inherent value in doing such. Inform group members that each will be offered the opportunity to finish the phrase "I am someone who" ten times, responding with a POSITIVE statement each time.

2. Review the sixteen words on border of handout to be used as phrase starters:

   feels . . . thinks . . . enjoys . . . has . . . believes . . . is . . . hopes to . . . once . . . collects . . . can . . . cherishes . . . wants to . . . strives to . . . will . . . values . . . cares to . . .

3. Encourage group members to offer a diverse presentation of self, including things related to: roles, leisure activities, work, family, pets, interests, personality traits, abilities, skills, accomplishments, etc. List categories on chalkboard.

4. Distribute handouts.

5. Allow 15-20 minutes for completion.

6. Provide an opportunity for group members to read lists aloud, encouraging feedback from peers.

7. Process benefits of portraying self in a positive light and learning about peers.

B. 1. Discuss the value in presenting oneself positively, recognizing the inherent value in doing such. Inform group members they will be offered the opportunity to finish the phrase "I am someone who" ten times, responding with a POSITIVE statement each time.

2. Review the sixteen words on border of handout to be used as phrase starters:

   feels . . . thinks . . . enjoys . . . has . . . believes . . . is . . . hopes to . . . once . . . collects . . . can . . . cherishes . . . wants to . . . strives to . . . will . . . values . . . cares to . . .

3. Encourage group members to offer a diverse presentation of self, including things related to: roles, leisure activities, work, family, pets, interests, personality traits, abilities, skills, accomplishments, etc. List this on categories on chalkboard.

4. Distribute handouts.

5. Allow 15-20 minutes for completion.

6. Collect and redistribute sheets so that each group member holds the work of someone else. Ask group members to read the list aloud, venturing a guess as to the author, and most importantly, stating the reason(s) for his/her guess.

7. When all discussion has ceased, ask the author to identify his/herself.

8. Process this activity by discussing the difficulty or barriers of writing and talking about positive self-statements.

Activity handout and facilitator's information adapted from submission by Maggie Moriarty, M.Ed., COTA/L, Bloomfield, CT.

POSITIVE *Affirmations*

are Self-Esteem Boosters!

1. I like myself because ________ ________ ________.	9. I consider myself a good ________ ________ ________.	17. I am most happy when ________ ________ ________.
2. I do ________ ________ ________ very well.	10. I like the way I feel about myself when I ________ ________.	18. My goals for the future are ________ ________ ________.
3. I feel good about ________ ________ ________.	11. What I really enjoy most is ________ ________ ________.	19. One of the many positive traits I have is ________ ________.
4. My friends would tell you I have a great ________ ________.	12. The person I look up to the most is ________ ________.	20. People often compliment me about ________ ________.
5. My favorite place is ________ ________ ________.	13. The one person that always makes me feel good about myself is ________.	21. My friends respect me because I always ________ ________.
6. ________ ________ ________ loves me!	14. I look good when ________ ________ ________.	22. I have a good sense of ________ ________ ________.
7. People say I am a good ________ ________ ________.	15. The color ________ ________ ________ looks great on me.	23. The two things I do best are ________ and ________.
8. I have been told that I have pretty ________ ________.	16. I have a natural talent for ________ ________ ________.	24. I know that I will be successful in life because I will ________ ________.

GENUINELY LIKING WHO YOU ARE IS THE CORE OF YOUR SELF-ESTEEM!!!

POSITIVE *Affirmations*

I. PURPOSE:

To increase self-esteem by acknowledging and accepting positive qualities about oneself.

II. GENERAL COMMENTS:

Affirmations can be a very powerful way of developing or restoring self-esteem. Acknowledging positive qualities in front of peers further augments one's self-esteem. It is important to differentiate between a healthy self-esteem and over-confidence or arrogance.

III. POSSIBLE ACTIVITIES:

A. 1. Prior to group photocopy handout and cut along perforated line, creating a deck of 24 cards.
2. Explain the concept of positive affirmations.
3. Arrange group members' seats in a semi-circle.
4. Place a chair in the middle of the semi-circle facing the group. On the chair place a deck of cards from the handout and a bowl of treats, e.g., pretzels, candy, gum.
5. Explain to the group that one by one, each group member will walk to the chair and pick the top card from the deck.
6. Each group member must finish the sentence on a personal level by reading aloud his/her answer to the group.
7. Initiate a round of applause after each group member has spoken.
8. Encourage each group member to award him/herself with one treat after completing the sentence.
9. Process by discussing the ease or difficulty group members experienced when doing this exercise. Ask how each group member can use positive affirmations in his/her personal life after the session is over.

B. 1. Distribute handouts explaining that developing or restoring a healthy self-esteem is an active process, rather than a passive one.
2. Give group members five minutes to complete entire handout.
3. Recruit volunteers to share the completed information using the 'WHO' Ice Breaker, page 59. As group members raise hands to respond to questions, ask each to read entire handout aloud, completing sentences. Make sure that all group members share (to ensure fairness) by adding additional 'WHO' Ice Breaker questions as needed. Applaud after each group member has spoken.
4. Ask group members to consider the importance of self-esteem. How important is it to spend time with people who have positive self-esteem? How do others maintain a healthy self-esteem? What can a healthy self-esteem enable one to do? How are self-esteem and success related?
5. Process by asking group members to set one realistic goal regarding the use of positive affirmations.

Activity handout and facilitator's information adapted from submission by Michele Vitelli, Motivational Instructor, Skippack, PA.

The HIV Infection/AIDS Quiz

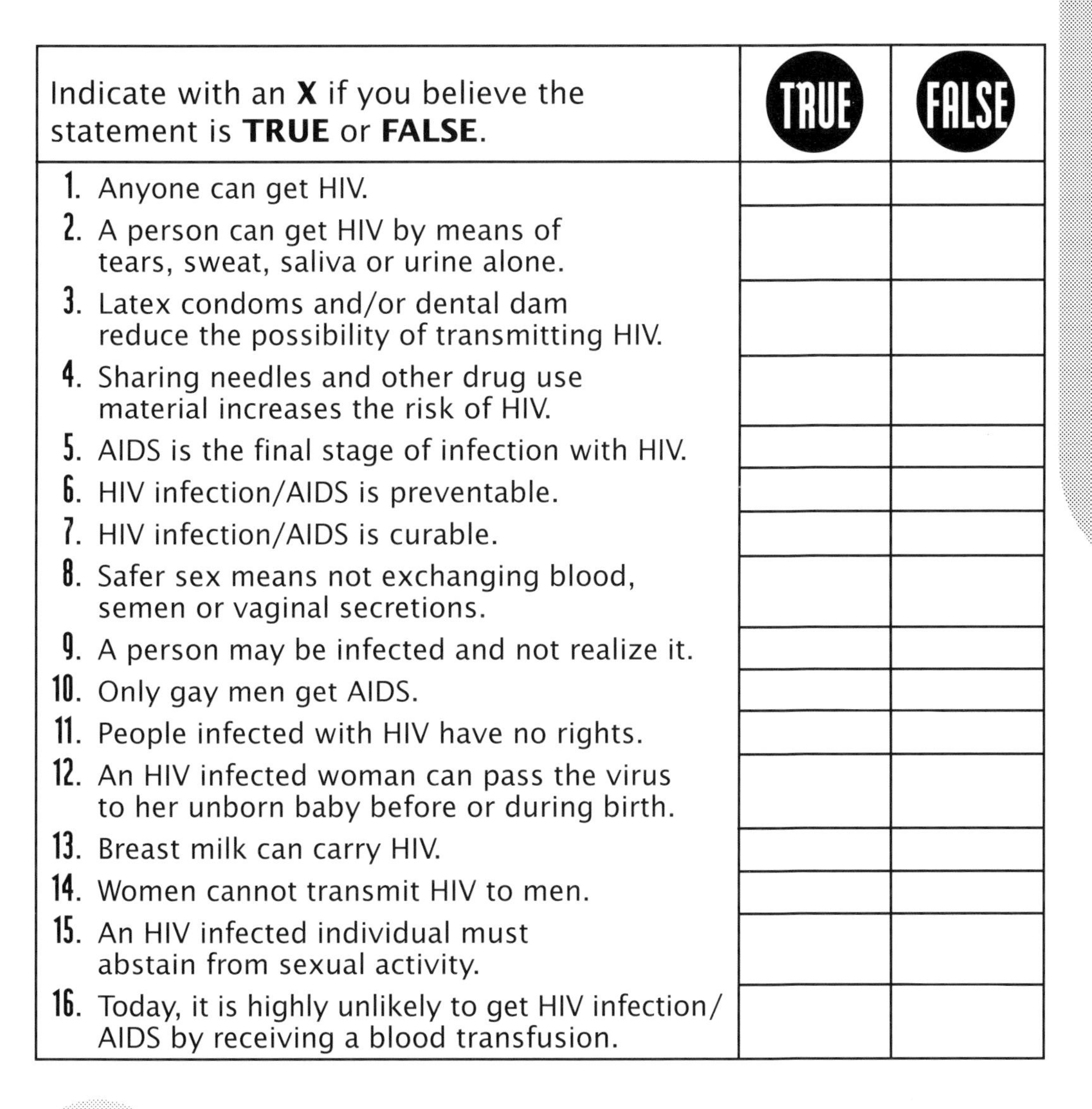

Indicate with an **X** if you believe the statement is **TRUE** or **FALSE**.	TRUE	FALSE
1. Anyone can get HIV.		
2. A person can get HIV by means of tears, sweat, saliva or urine alone.		
3. Latex condoms and/or dental dam reduce the possibility of transmitting HIV.		
4. Sharing needles and other drug use material increases the risk of HIV.		
5. AIDS is the final stage of infection with HIV.		
6. HIV infection/AIDS is preventable.		
7. HIV infection/AIDS is curable.		
8. Safer sex means not exchanging blood, semen or vaginal secretions.		
9. A person may be infected and not realize it.		
10. Only gay men get AIDS.		
11. People infected with HIV have no rights.		
12. An HIV infected woman can pass the virus to her unborn baby before or during birth.		
13. Breast milk can carry HIV.		
14. Women cannot transmit HIV to men.		
15. An HIV infected individual must abstain from sexual activity.		
16. Today, it is highly unlikely to get HIV infection/AIDS by receiving a blood transfusion.		

Are you at risk for becoming infected with HIV? (Circle any that apply:)

Share needles

Practice vaginal and anal sex without a condom

Many sex partners

PRACTICE ORAL SEX WITHOUT A CONDOM OR DENTAL DAM

Use natural skin or lamb skin condoms

Hemophiliac or hemophilia treatments
(particularly before 1986)

History of blood transfusions
(particularly before 1986)

Sexual partner of an HIV infected person

Thinking that if you ignore HIV/AIDS, it will go away

Thinking that if you don't talk about it, it won't happen

Thinking that it could never happen to you.

The HIV Infection/AIDS Quiz

I. PURPOSE:

To increase general awareness of HIV infection and sexual responsibility.

II. GENERAL COMMENTS:

HIV infection is currently a life-threatening infectious disease with no known cure. The mounting increase in HIV infection worldwide, has led authorities to focus on prevention as essential in stopping this devastating disease.

HIV (Human Immuno-deficiency Virus) is a blood-borne, retro virus that attacks the immune system and eventually seriously impairs it. The primary source of infection is through sexual contact. (Less than 3% of all AIDS cases are a result of contaminated blood.)

The immune system is what protects an individual from becoming severely ill. The HIV enters the immune system, and attacks the CD4 (T-4) cells that help fight off infection. Eventually an individual has too few cells left to fight off infections and is at risk for becoming very ill and dying.

AIDS (Acquired Immune Deficiency Syndrome) is the final stage of infection in HIV.

The facilitator of these activities should have a basic knowledge of sexuality and HIV/AIDS.

For further information:

CDC National HIV and AIDS hotline – 800 / 342-2437 (24 hours, 7 days a week)
Spanish service – 800 / 344-7432 (7 days a week - 8 AM – 2 AM EST)
TTY (Deaf) Service – 800 / 243-7889 (Monday through Friday 10 AM – 10 PM EST)

III. POSSIBLE ACTIVITIES:

A. 1. Introduce topic of AIDS/HIV.
   2. Distribute handouts and instruct group members to complete top section.
   3. Review the answers as a group using answer key below as a guide.
   4. Discuss risk factors by asking group members to choose a listed one and explain it to the group.
   5. Offer additional information as the group requests.
   6. Process by discussing the importance of taking responsibility for one's sexual health.

B. 1. Divide group into pairs.
   2. Distribute handouts and instruct pairs to complete together.
   3. Review as a group offering additional information as needed using answer key below as a guide.
   4. Facilitate discussion of what preventative medicine is, offering ideas such as nutritional supplements, dental check ups, exercise, stress management, etc. Then, include discussion of sexual health.
   5. Discuss prevention behaviors such as abstinence, "dry activities", "safer sex". Clearly outline unsafe practices.

Answer key

1. T	5. T	9. T	13. T
2. F	6. T	10. F	14. F
3. T	7. F	11. F	15. F
4. T	8. T	12. T	16. T

Activity handout and facilitator's information adapted from submission by Laura M. Grogan, OTR/L, Washington D.C. in collaboration with Dr. Ann E. Weeks, of Healing Strategies for Life's Passages, Louisville , KY.

Your Sexuality - Myths and Realities

Many people are unaware of the truths about sexuality and accept the myths. These "missing pieces" can affect your ability to make decisions and to have healthy sexual experiences. How much do you know about your own sexuality? Answer the following 20 questions regarding sexual myths.

Agree (A)	Disagree (D)	
______	______	1. Alcohol is probably the best known of all aphrodisiacs.
______	______	2. Masturbation is mostly practiced by the young and immature; it normally ends after marriage.
______	______	3. Ejaculation and orgasm are the same thing.
______	______	4. The average size of the erect human penis is about six inches.
______	______	5. Coitus interruptus - withdrawal of the penis from the vagina just before ejaculation - is a quite effective form of birth control.
______	______	6. AIDS is primarily a sexually transmitted disease that can be spread in other ways.
______	______	7. Women with large breasts tend to be more sexually responsive than women with small breasts.
______	______	8. A woman cannot get pregnant the first time she has sex.
______	______	9. The rhythm method is not as effective as the birth control method.
______	______	10. Individuals with larger penises tend to better satisfy their lovers.
______	______	11. Homosexuality should be regarded as an illness.
______	______	12. It doesn't hurt someone to get aroused and not have sex.
______	______	13. The clitoris, the most sensitive spot on most women's bodies, is positioned in such a way that it is easy to stimulate during normal intercourse.
______	______	14. A form of safer sex is self-gratification.
______	______	15. Women are usually more easily aroused and can engage in satisfactory intercourse more rapidly than men.
______	______	16. Communication barriers are key factors in sexual problems.
______	______	17. For most men, the frenulum (the area underneath and just behind the glands or head of the penis) is usually the most sensitive spot.
______	______	18. Oral-genital contact should be regarded as an acceptable form of foreplay.
______	______	19. STDs (Sexually Transmitted Diseases) are contracted only by people of lower socioeconomic status.
______	______	20. Polls show that young adults state that sexual desire is their primary desire in getting involved in sexual activity.

Healthy sexual experiences require maturity and knowledge.

Your Sexuality - Myths and Realities

I. PURPOSE:

To increase knowledge of sexual myths and realities.

To develop a healthy attitude toward sexual health and behavior.

II. GENERAL COMMENTS:

People's attitudes towards sex, sex roles and marriage have experienced significant changes during the last decade. Despite the new openness about sexual topics, many people continue to be shy or ambivalent about sexual intimacy. Unfortunately, many myths still exist and need to be dispelled to allow for healthy decisions and satisfying experiences. Taking responsibility for one's sexual expression includes developing a healthy attitude and behavior as well as increasing knowledge of sexual myths and realities. The facilitator of these activities should have a basic knowledge of sexuality and be comfortable with the topic.

III. POSSIBLE ACTIVITIES:

A. 1. Distribute handouts.

2. Encourage each group member to answer as many questions as able.
3. Before starting group discussion, acknowledge comfort level (or discomfort level) of the group with the topic of sexuality.
4. Facilitate discussion by asking members to share answers and offer correct responses as needed.
5. Discuss with group members the following questions:
   a. How do you feel about answering the questions?
   b. Were you surprised with some of the questions? Answers?
   c. What influences did your upbringing have on your attitude toward sex? Positive or negative?
   d. Are there any changes about your sexual attitude or behavior that you would like to make? Do you know how to go about making those changes?
6. Process the session by discussing insights gained from this activity.

B. 1. Distribute handouts and read each statement one by one as group members complete. Offer correct answers as needed.

2. Write the following topics on a flip chart:
   a. Masturbation
   b. Oral-genital sex
   c. Homosexuality
   d. Sexual communication
   e. Male sex organs
   f. Female sex organs
   g. Aphrodisiacs
   h. Birth control
   i. Sexually transmitted diseases
3. Ask which topics the group members would like to address. Consider the group's level of comfort and time availability.
4. Explore group knowledge regarding the chosen topic(s) and provide information accordingly.
5. Process by asking group members how this session affected either their sexual knowledge or attitude.

ANSWER KEY: A = Agree D = Disagree

1.D 2.D 3.D 4.A 5.D 6.A 7.D 8.D 9.A 10.D 11.D 12.A 13.D 14.A 15.D 16.A 17.A 18.A 19.D 20.D

Activity handout and facilitator's information adapted from submission by Hector L. Merced, OTR/L
in collaboration with Deena Baenan, MA, COTA/L, Cleveland, OH.

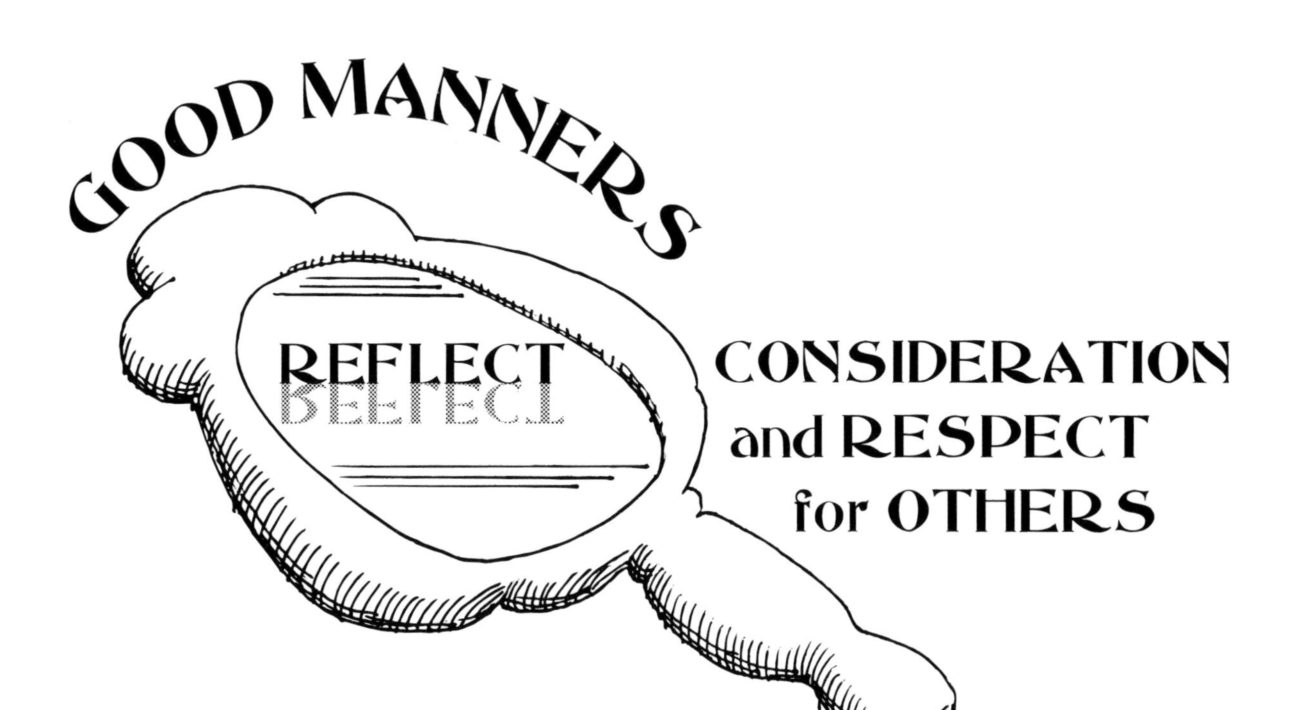

I COULD IMPROVE IN:

____ 1. Making introductions
____ 2. Respecting individual differences
____ 3. Using tactful conversation
____ 4. Routinely thanking others
____ 5. Using table manners
____ 6. Entertaining others
____ 7. Being a considerate guest
____ 8. Making an apology
____ 9. Conversing and listening to others
____ 10. Using good manners at work
____ 11. Dressing appropriately
____ 12. Repaying past favors
____ 13. Showing respect for authority figures
____ 14. Using good manners with family members
____ 15. Meeting new people
____ 16. Writing social and/or business letters
____ 17. Planning special occasions
____ 18. Other ____

GOOD MANNERS

I. PURPOSE:

To increase socialization by reviewing good manners in daily life and the individuals' needs for improvement.

II. GENERAL COMMENTS:

Good manners are based on consideration and respect for others in a variety of situations.

III. POSSIBLE ACTIVITIES:

A. 1. Pass a hand mirror to participants asking each to reflect on one way in which each sees themselves as mannerly. Encourage responses which reflect individuality and creativity. Examples can also be given.

2. Distribute handouts and ask participants to check areas for needed improvement. These may be verbally shared with the group.

3. Facilitate a discussion of handout. Questions might include:

   Why introduce people?
   Why make an apology?
   Why use tactful speech?
   Why be mannerly to your family?
   What is a considerate guest?
   How does one meet new people and encourage friendships?
   What would be good manners at work?
   What entertaining or future event would you like to plan?

4. Ask group participants with the same needs to brainstorm in an effort to problem solve.

5. Regroup and share responses and conclusions.

6. Compile a list of other good manners.

7. Process by asking group members what might be a positive outcome of good manners.

B. 1. Distribute handouts and ask group members to complete.

2. Determine group needs based on their responses and your observations.

3. Focus on specific topic(s), e.g., 16. *Writing social and/or business letters*, asking them to write a business letter for a group critique - or - 12. *Repaying past favors*, asking pairs to role-play repaying a favor or past kindness.

4. If additional time, ask the group for suggested situations to role-play.

5. Process by asking group members to set realistic goals to improve manners.

Activity handout and facilitator's information adapted from submission by Bettie Michelson, OTR/L, M.S., Waukesha, WI.

Social Skills 4 LIFE

1. How do you plan your social life?

____

____

____

____

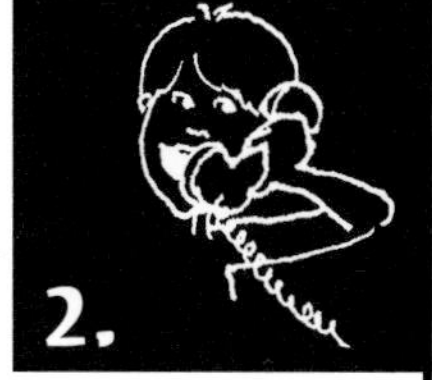

2. How do you make and keep friends?

____

____

____

____

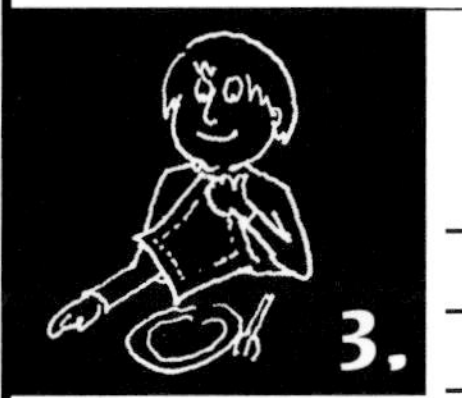

3. What good manners do you routinely use?

____

____

____

____

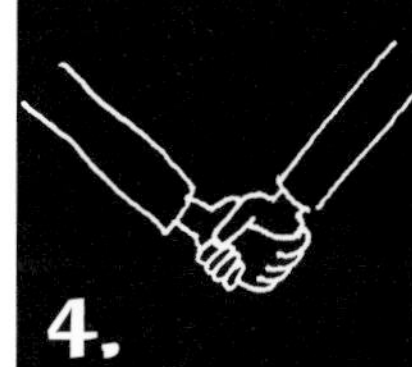

4. Name some guidelines you use in making introductions.

____

____

____

____

5. How do you initiate a conversation?

____

____

____

____

6. Describe the entertaining you like, and do best.

____

____

____

____

7. How do you groom and dress for success?

____

____

____

____

8. How do you broaden your interests, knowledge, and current awareness?

____

____

____

9. How do you socialize in a group?

____

____

____

____

10. How do you show respect to your authority figures?

____

____

____

____

I. PURPOSE:

To assess individual social skills and to expand social awareness and growth.

II. GENERAL COMMENTS:

Social skills can be refined throughout a lifetime to bring a greater satisfaction to all human interactions.

III. POSSIBLE ACTIVITIES:

A. 1. Distribute handouts and extra paper as needed. Instruct group members to complete.
   2. Encourage participants to verbally share written responses.
   3. Introduce related topics such as the relationship of social skills to self-confidence, career success, success in entertaining, popularity, joining groups or organizations, etc.
   4. Compile a group list of "the top ten" desirable manners.
   5. Have resource material available for the various aspects of social skills. Some material may be assigned for presentations to the group.
   6. Encourage participants to describe someone they know with good social skills.

B. 1. Distribute handouts and ask group members to complete. Discuss as a group.
   2. Plan role-plays of social situations, such as making introductions, initiating a conversation, going to a group function alone, making a complaint, etc. Briefly described, they could be assigned or randomly drawn. If available, videotape for feedback, if all group members agree.
   3. Explore information on community resources, activities, organizations, special events and sites of interest to increase social experiences.
   4. Suggest that participants initiate thoughtful acts for each other. In the next session, ask those receiving the kindnesses, to share their experiences with the group.

Activity handout and facilitator's information adapted from submission by Bettie Michelson, OTR/L, M.S., Waukesha, WI.

ORGANIZE yourself by learning the art of . . . DELEGATION.

del´•e•gāt: TO ENTRUST TO ANOTHER

A. Check one area of your life from which you could benefit from delegating:

_____ home responsibilities
_____ work responsibilities
_____ family responsibilities
_____ community/civic responsibilities
_____ other ______________________________

____

____

B. In that area, what is one task or job you can delegate, that you aren't now?

____

____

C. What are 3 barriers that prevent you from delegating today?

1) ______________________________
2) ______________________________
3) ______________________________

D. What are 3 steps you would take to delegate this job or task?

1) ______________________________
2) ______________________________
3) ______________________________

E. If you do delegate this task or job, name 3 ways you will benefit.

1) ______________________________
2) ______________________________
3) ______________________________

F. Who has the skills to do this job or task, to whom you would feel comfortable delegating?

____

G. Name 3 ways that the person you're delegating to might benefit.

1) ______________________________
2) ______________________________
3) ______________________________

GOAL : ______________________________

____

DELEGATION

I. PURPOSE:

To improve stress management by learning the organizational skill of delegation.

II. GENERAL COMMENTS:

Delegation, the ability to entrust another, is an important organizational skill that has significant benefits. Possible benefits of delegation would be: development of delegatees, efficiency, leadership, increased team or family enthusiasm, opportunity for delegatee to gain experience, accountability, improved family or team trust and evolution of team or family members. All of these benefits might have direct or indirect effects on stress management. Delegating might be an uncomfortable process because of the actual or perceived negative perspectives. The barriers to delegation might be: a feeling that it's better to be on your own, approval need, one is afraid of the response of the delegatee, refusal of the delegatee, risk aversion, irrational self-talk, ego of delegator, feeling replaceable, supermartyr syndrome (I have to do it all).

III. POSSIBLE ACTIVITIES:

A. 1. Distribute handouts. Introduce topic using above stated PURPOSE and GENERAL COMMENTS.

2. Discuss each area of responsibilities thoroughly from Section A. Ask group members if it is possible to delegate in one area well, but not in another. How does the inability to delegate relate to stress?
3. Continue to complete handout together as a group discussing examples from the group. Instruct group members to wait until later in the session before completing the goals section.
4. Write on the board the following three categories: Benefits to me, Benefits to delegatee, My barriers.
5. Facilitate discussion of each of the categories by listing group members contributions.
6. Instruct group members to write realistic goals and share.
7. Process by asking group members how delegating would improve stress and time management.

B. 1. Discuss the concept of delegating.

2. Ask group members to list leaders that are great delegators. The list may come from personal examples, political figures, movie characters, etc. Discuss what the consequences might be if these people did not possess the organizational skill of delegating.
3. Distribute handouts.
4. Use one group example to illustrate how to complete this handout.
5. Instruct group members to complete individually.
6. Use role-plays to encourage open discussion of responsibilities and to practice delegating.
7. List on a dry/erase board "Tips to successful delegating" (such as, select people who can accept responsibility, remember that the person you pick to do the job may not do it as well as you, assign low-risk projects first, check back with the delegatee as often as you need to, give a specific due date or time when the job needs to be completed) with the group's input.
8. Process by asking group members how the ability to delegate correlates with stress management, effective leadership, healthy relationships and time management.

Activity handout and facilitator's information adapted from submission by
Marie Calabrese, RN, MA, and Mary Beth Modic, RN, MSN, Cleveland, OH.

Letting Go of other's expectations

LETTING GO OF THE NEED TO LIVE YOUR LIFE ACCORDING TO OTHER PEOPLE'S EXPECTATIONS is a skill that will result in personal freedoms.
Ask yourself…Do I follow my "shoulds" or my inner voice?

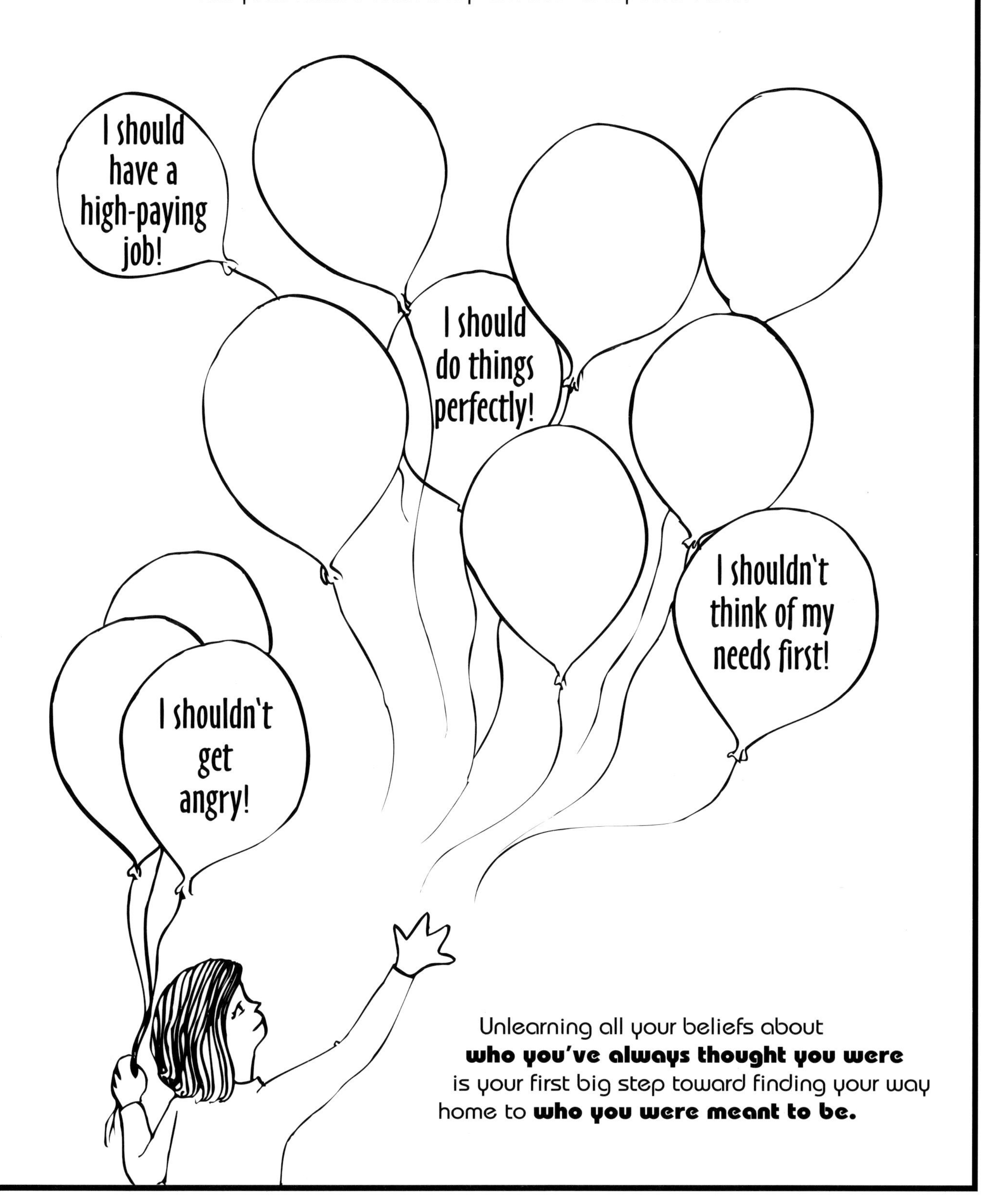

Unlearning all your beliefs about **who you've always thought you were** is your first big step toward finding your way home to **who you were meant to be.**

Letting Go of other's expectations

I. PURPOSE:

To identify some of the beliefs and subsequent behavior patterns that cause stress, and discover whether they are truly intrinsic beliefs or beliefs adopted without questioning.

To increase awareness that one can choose to "let go" of these behavior patterns and beliefs.

II. GENERAL COMMENTS:

Learning to "let go" is a skill, and is a key to happiness and freedom. The *shoulds* of our lives can weigh us down and feel burdensome and repressive. That freedom is symbolized by the balloons which are being let go, one after another. The less we tie ourselves to other people's expectations the more in control of our lives we are, because we have freed ourselves of the emotional trauma that results when expectations are not met. This freedom allows us to become "our own" people, to evolve into individuals with "our own" thoughts, beliefs and values.

III. POSSIBLE ACTIVITIES:

A. 1. Discuss the concept of "letting go" in terms of the need to live our lives according to other people's (and society's) expectations of who we *should* or *shouldn't* be, versus listening to and following our own "inner voice" (hearts).

2. Distribute handouts.

3. Ask group members to write personal examples of *shoulds* or *shouldn'ts* in the blank balloons. Offer one topic as appropriate to the group for additional focus, e.g., alcohol dependence - I *should* be able to have one drink, e.g., body image - I *should* be 20 pounds less.

4. Ask group members to share examples.

5. Discuss the benefits of identifying these types of behavior patterns and choosing to "let go" of them in favor of listening to our hearts (inner voice) more.

6. Process by discussing how to take less heed of others' beliefs about who we *should* be.

B. 1. Discuss the concept of "letting go" in terms of the need to live our lives according to other people's (and society's) expectations of who we *should* or *shouldn't* be, versus listening to and following our own inner voice.

2. Distribute handouts.

3. Ask group members to complete the handout .

4. Instruct group members to make two lists on the back of the handout. The first is a list of *shoulds* that arise from personal beliefs; the second is a list of *shoulds* that are suspect to be 'second-hand' beliefs - in other words, beliefs that were handed down from someone else, e.g., parents, church/temple, school, etc.

5. Encourage group members to share one *should* from each list.

6. Process by discussing the benefits of identifying our *shoulds* and *shouldn'ts* and asking ourselves where they came from, in terms of "letting go" of any and all beliefs that are not serving us well.

Activity handout and facilitator's information adapted from submission by Diane Hausler, LSW, Fairview Park, OH.

Letting Go of the need to control

Letting go of the need to control people in relationships is a skill, and a key to happiness and freedom.

Here are some choices you can make every day to improve the quality of your relationships with others and yourself.

Fill in some examples from your own life, of controlling or being controlled, in the blank boxes.

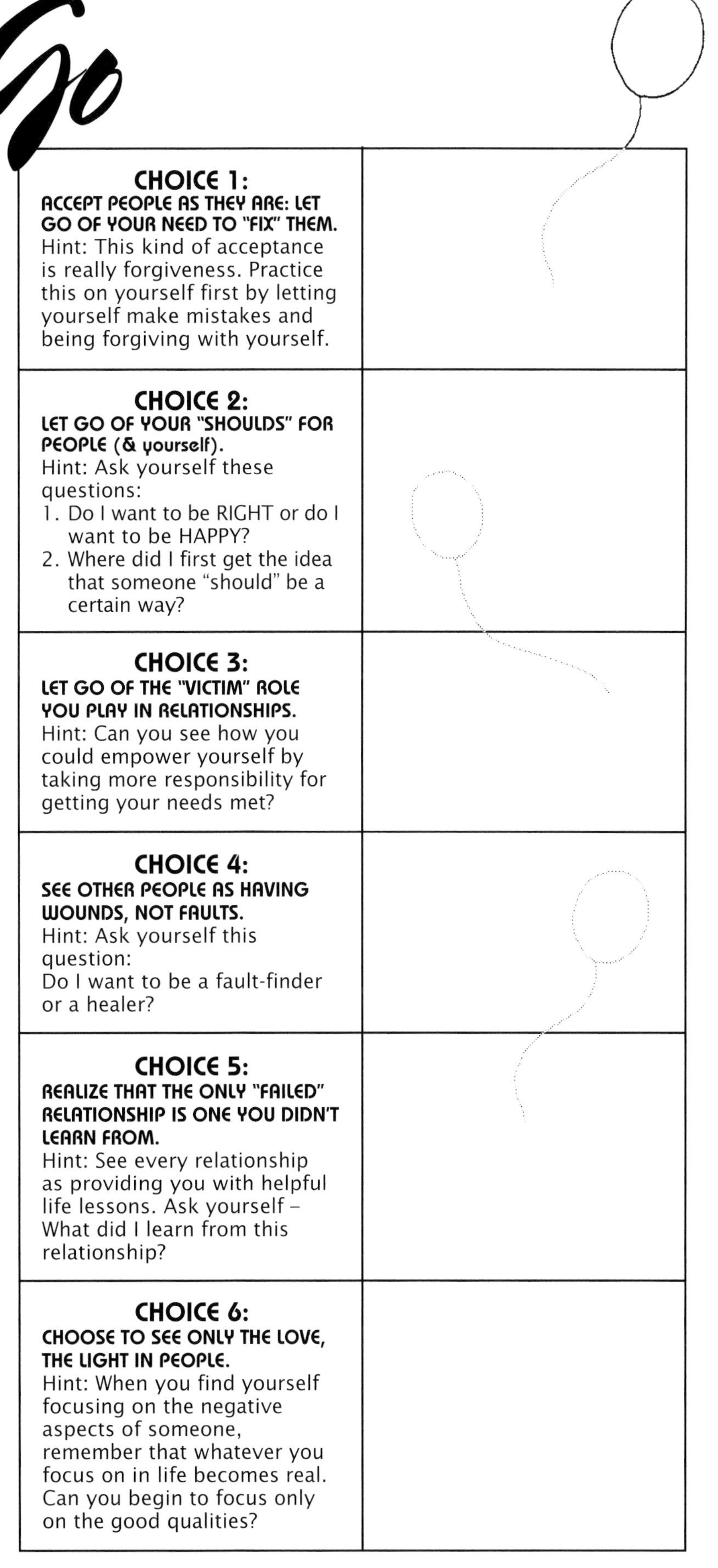

CHOICE 1: **ACCEPT PEOPLE AS THEY ARE: LET GO OF YOUR NEED TO "FIX" THEM.** Hint: This kind of acceptance is really forgiveness. Practice this on yourself first by letting yourself make mistakes and being forgiving with yourself.	
CHOICE 2: **LET GO OF YOUR "SHOULDS" FOR PEOPLE (& yourself).** Hint: Ask yourself these questions: 1. Do I want to be RIGHT or do I want to be HAPPY? 2. Where did I first get the idea that someone "should" be a certain way?	
CHOICE 3: **LET GO OF THE "VICTIM" ROLE YOU PLAY IN RELATIONSHIPS.** Hint: Can you see how you could empower yourself by taking more responsibility for getting your needs met?	
CHOICE 4: **SEE OTHER PEOPLE AS HAVING WOUNDS, NOT FAULTS.** Hint: Ask yourself this question: Do I want to be a fault-finder or a healer?	
CHOICE 5: **REALIZE THAT THE ONLY "FAILED" RELATIONSHIP IS ONE YOU DIDN'T LEARN FROM.** Hint: See every relationship as providing you with helpful life lessons. Ask yourself – What did I learn from this relationship?	
CHOICE 6: **CHOOSE TO SEE ONLY THE LOVE, THE LIGHT IN PEOPLE.** Hint: When you find yourself focusing on the negative aspects of someone, remember that whatever you focus on in life becomes real. Can you begin to focus only on the good qualities?	

ONE MORE HINT: Try to see everyone you meet as a teacher who has been sent to give you just what you need to grow!

Letting Go of the need to control

I. PURPOSE:

To identify behavior patterns associated with the need to control people that oftentimes cause stress in relationships.

To increase awareness that one can choose to "let go" of these behavior patterns and beliefs.

II. GENERAL COMMENTS: This handout may be used in conjunction with MEDITATION ON LETTING GO OF CONTROL (page 53).

Learning to "let go" is a skill, and it is a key to happiness and freedom. The need to control people is a complex one and often results in dissatisfying relationships and stress. The less we tie ourselves to predicted outcomes, the more in control of our lives we are, because we have freed ourselves of the emotional trauma that results when our expectations are not met.

III. POSSIBLE ACTIVITIES:

A. 1. Discuss the concept of "letting go" in terms of *controlling* versus *accepting* people just as they are.

2. Distribute handouts. Instruct group members to complete the handout with examples of controlling people or of being controlled. Offer example to group, if needed, e.g., Choice 1: *When I tell my sister(s) what to do or how to handle certain situations,* or *when my sister judges me and advises me on matters when I don't request her help.*

3. Ask group members to share examples.

4. Discuss benefits of identifying these types of behavior patterns and choosing to "let them go".

B. 1. Divide group into pairs or triads.

2. Distribute handouts, assigning each subgroup one choice.

3. Instruct each subgroup to discuss the assigned choice thoroughly. Write the following list of thought provoking questions on the dry erase board for all to see and respond.

   a. How does this *choice* relate to your present relationships?

   b. Was this a behavior you noticed/observed while growing up?

   c. What are the barriers or obstacles (if any) you see in implementing this behavior today?

4. Ask each group to give a small report on their subgroup's experience.

5. Facilitate discussion of potential benefits of following hints and making healthy choices.

6. Process by asking group members to identify one *choice* that can be realistically implemented after the group session is completed.

Activity handout and facilitator's information adapted from submission by Diane Hausler, LSW, Fairview Park, OH.

Managing StReSS

Meditation is a state of restful alertness that is easy to learn. It has no religious overtones; there is no belief required. Continued practice will bring into your life such physical benefits as increased energy, lower blood pressure and relief from StReSS headaches. Perhaps even more importantly, you will experience a growing awareness of your innate goodness and an inner calm that will help you to weather the emotional storms of life.

Here are the general instructions:

1. Sit quietly with your eyes closed.
2. Repeat your mantra (this can be any word that is neutral for you, such as "peace" or "one" or the traditional "om") whenever you think of it. Don't force it, just listen to it.
3. Allow your thoughts to move through your mind like clouds across the sky - don't push them away.
4. Whenever you notice you have gotten lost in your thoughts again, gently reintroduce your mantra.
5. Repeat this procedure throughout your meditation without judging it. Like training a puppy, keep patiently bringing it back home.

Remember not to judge your ability to meditate.
The relaxation response will occur whether or not you think you are doing it successfully.

The practice of meditation brings improvement, over time, in each of the following areas. Which of these areas do you want to focus on?

What is my usual *energy level*, and how does stress affect it? ☐	Which do I identify with more – *what I do in my life* or *who I AM inside?* ☐	How able am I to act *spontaneously* really enjoying the moment? ☐	How long do I tend to hold on to *anger* or *hurt feelings?* ☐
How often do I have a feeling of *inner peace*, of "everything's all right in my world"? ☐	How do I *respond emotionally and physically* to stressful situations? ☐	How would people react if they saw *the real me* – a. approach me eagerly? b. recoil in horror? ☐	How *flexible* am I when confronted with a sudden change of plans? ☐

Meditation is a powerful tool for managing stress when practiced regularly.

I. PURPOSE:

To reduce stress through the regular practice of meditation.

II. GENERAL COMMENTS:

Meditation practice has been proved to provide many physical and emotional benefits. It is a state of restful alertness, in which deep relaxation is attained by focusing on a meaningless word called a mantra. This can be any word that is neutral for the practitioner, such as "peace" or "one" or the traditional "om". Optimum results are achieved through meditating twice daily for twenty minutes each, once in the morning before eating and a second time before dinner.

III. POSSIBLE ACTIVITIES:

This handout can be used in conjunction with MEDITATION SCRIPTS, pages 52 and 53.

A. 1. Read the description of meditation to the group from the above stated GENERAL COMMENTS.
2. Ask if anyone has had any experience with meditation, and emphasize that only the technique will be taught today. Any subsequent questions will need to be answered through the many books and tapes available on this subject, e.g., Minding the Body, Mending the Mind by Joan Borysenko.
3. Ask the group members to get comfortable, close their eyes and listen to the steps that will be read to them on how to meditate. Each group member must choose a word to use as a mantra.
4. Now have group begin to meditate, repeating their mantra for one minute, with eyes still closed.
5. At the end of one minute say, "Now, slowly open your eyes" and ask if anyone felt some stillness.
6. Then say, "Now we will close our eyes again and meditate for ten minutes". (Or twenty if you have time.)
7. At the end of the ten minutes say "Now, slowly open your eyes" and ask if anyone felt any quietness.
8. End by saying, "This is how we meditate. Twenty minutes in the morning and twenty minutes in the evening is optimal. If that is impossible, practice for at least a half hour sometime during the day."
9. Distribute handouts for reinforcement and ask group members to complete bottom section of the handout and bring to next session.

B. 1. Distribute handouts and review.
2. Ask group members to complete bottom section and discuss in which areas individuals wish to focus.
3. Explain that the practice of meditation brings improvement, over time, in each of these areas. It is a powerful tool for managing stress when practiced regularly.
4. Ask group members to share responses to the three questions that each found to be the most important.
5. Facilitate brief meditation by asking that group members get comfortable, close their eyes and listen to the steps that will be read to them on how to meditate. Each group member must choose a word to use as a mantra.
6. Now have group begin to meditate, repeating their mantra for one minute, with eyes still closed.
7. At the end of one minute say, "Now, slowly open your eyes" and ask if anyone felt some stillness.
8. Then say, "Now we will close our eyes again and meditate for ten minutes". (Or twenty if you have time.)
9. At the end of the ten minutes say "Now, slowly open your eyes" and ask if anyone felt any quietness.
10. End by saying, "This is how we meditate. Twenty minutes in the morning and twenty minutes in the evening is optimal. If that is impossible, practice for at least a half hour sometime during the day."
11. Discuss how meditation might bring positive change into specific areas of one's life.

Activity handout and facilitator's information adapted from submission by Diane Hausler, LSW, Fairview Park, OH.

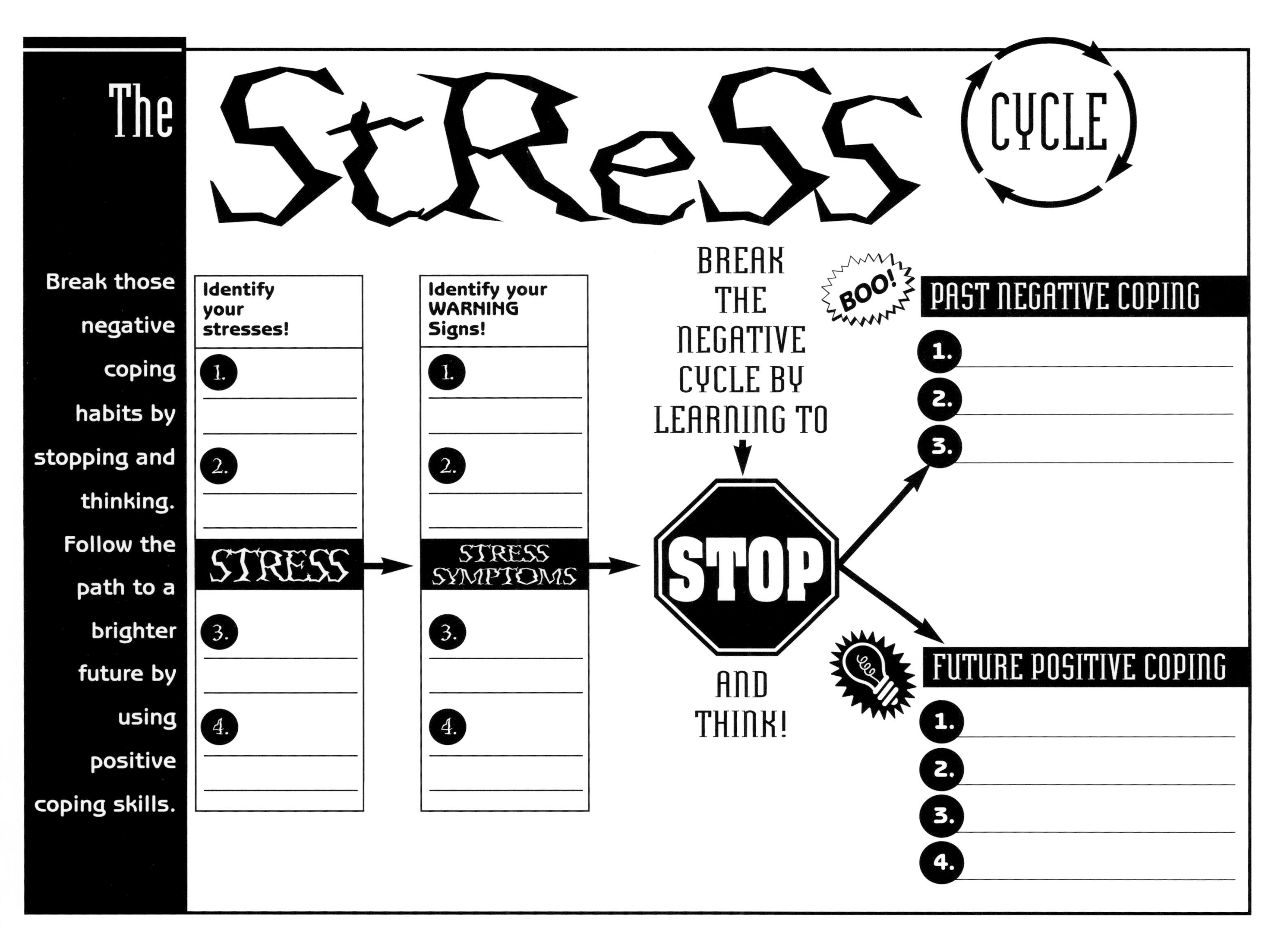
The StReSS CYCLE
Break those negative coping habits by stopping and thinking. Follow the path to a brighter future by using positive coping skills.
Identify your stresses!
1.
2.
STRESS
3.
4.
Identify your WARNING Signs!
1.
2.
STRESS SYMPTOMS
3.
4.
BREAK THE NEGATIVE CYCLE BY LEARNING TO
STOP
AND THINK!
BOO!
PAST NEGATIVE COPING
1.
2.
3.
FUTURE POSITIVE COPING
1.
2.
3.
4.

The STRESS CYCLE

I. PURPOSE:

To identify one's stressors as well as the personal stress symptoms that occur.

To increase awareness of negative coping habits and the options of positive coping skills.

II. GENERAL COMMENTS:

Effective stress management has many components. First is identifying the stressors. Next is recognizing the personal stress symptoms or the "warning signs" that our bodies give us telling us it's time to relax. Then, we cope in a negative or positive way. Negative coping skills can become bad habits, e.g., drinking alcohol --- whereas positive coping skills can literally be our lifesavers, e.g., exercise. This handout emphasizes breaking negative coping patterns and learning positive coping skills. THE STRESS MANAGEMENT CONTRACT (page 57), may be used in conjunction with this handout.

III. POSSIBLE ACTIVITIES:

A. 1. Define "stressors".
   2. Brainstorm with group different everyday stressors, marking on chalkboard.
   3. Define "stress symptoms" (warning signs) and how they are our body's way of telling us that we need to relax.
   4. Distribute handouts and ask group members to complete.
   5. Ask for volunteers to disclose some personal warning signs, and how these symptoms affect them mentally, emotionally, physically or spiritually.
   6. Elicit disclosure of some negative coping examples, pointing out how repetition of negative coping leads to habits, i.e., someone might have a drinking problem. When stress symptoms become active, the first thought is to have a drink to relax. Every time this person drinks, it reinforces this negative habit.
   7. Problem solve positive coping skills and discuss as a group.
   8. Process benefits of importance of recognizing warning signs of stress and coping in a positive way.

B. 1. Facilitate discussion of identifying stressors as the first step of a stress management plan.
   2. Distribute handouts and ask group members to complete the cycle through the past negative coping sections, leaving the future positive coping section blank.
   3. Divide group into pairs. Ask partners to exchange handouts and to try to fill in the future positive coping list for their partner.
   4. When completed, ask them to share ideas.
   5. Process activity by recognizing the importance of STOPPING and THINKING when a stress symptom appears, to break negative coping habits.

Activity handout and facilitator's information adapted from submission by Pamela A. Joy, COTA/L, Barberton, OH.

STRESS Pleasure HIERARCHY

Think about the various stressful and pleasurable things that happen to you regularly.
Enter each at the appropriate number of points of stress and pleasure
you feel when each of these events occur.

0 = the least pleasurable or stressful
100 = the most pleasurable or stressful

Try to fill in as many of the 20 items in each column as possible.

STRESSORS		MOST ↕ LEAST	Pleasures	
100	______	MOST	100	______
95	______		95	______
90	______		90	______
85	______		85	______
80	______		80	______
75	______		75	______
70	______		70	______
65	______		65	______
60	______		60	______
55	______		55	______
50	______		50	______
45	______		45	______
40	______		40	______
35	______		35	______
30	______		30	______
25	______		25	______
20	______		20	______
15	______		15	______
10	______	LEAST	10	______
5	______		5	______
0	______		0	______

IT IS IMPORTANT TO STRIVE FOR A GOOD BALANCE BETWEEN STRESSORS and *Pleasures.*

STRESS - *Pleasure* HIERARCHY

I. PURPOSE:

To determine how intensely we think we respond to daily stressors and to the parts of our life we designate as pleasurable.

To increase recognition of how pleasure is essential to well-being and to reducing sense of stress.

To increase realization that daily pleasures do occur and can decrease stress substantially.

II. GENERAL COMMENTS:

The body will respond to stress the same way, whether the stressor is positive (something enjoyable happening) or negative (something upsetting happening). The body will respond differently, however, to the intensity of any particular stressor(s). We often respond to small stressors as if they were major problems. If we react to all stressors, large and small, as though they were large, we may be setting ourselves up to be stressed unnecessarily. By becoming aware of HOW MUCH stress or pleasure we feel from any one particular event, we can adjust our responses accordingly. Recognition of the magnitude of the stressor and permitting ourselves to enjoy pleasures, despite the presence of stress, offers two strategies to keep our stress levels in check.

III. POSSIBLE ACTIVITIES:

A. 1. Distribute handouts.

2. Discuss concept as outlined in the above stated GENERAL COMMENTS. Offer the following example:

   20 in the STRESSOR column might be "needing to wash dishes late at night" while 80 in the PLEASURES column might be "listening to a favorite piece of music".

3. Instruct group members to complete the handout, filling in as many as possible, but not worrying if every line isn't completed.

4. Choose a few of the questions listed below for a group discussion.

   a. Do you have an equal balance between the number of stressors identified versus the number of pleasures you have identified?

   b. Do you have an enormous amount of stressors listed and almost no pleasures?

   c. Are most of your stressors at one end of the scale or the other?

   d. Are your pleasures sufficiently enjoyable and numerous to counteract the intensity of the stressors you listed?

   e. If you have all pleasures listed and no stressors indicated, is this an accurate reflection of your current lifestyle? If not, how would you change your answers to make them more realistic? If yes, are the pleasures you indicated, sufficiently substantial to counteract possible future stressors?

   f. What additional pleasures can you add to your list to diffuse the intensity of the stressors?

5. Process by discussing ways to counteract stressors with pleasures, e.g., listening to favorite music while washing dishes late at night.

B. 1. Distribute handouts.

2. Discuss concept as outlined in the above stated GENERAL COMMENTS.

3. Instruct group members to complete the handout, filling in as many as possible, but not worrying if every line isn't completed.

4. Facilitate a discussion of the group, posing the question "What can you do to decrease the amount of stress in your life or in any one of the major stressors you listed?"

5. Next, ask and discuss "What can you do to increase the amount of pleasure you have in your life?" or "How can you add in one to three pleasurable activities into your daily and/or weekly schedule?"

6. If time permits, ask the following: "Are you engaging in the things you listed as pleasurable on a regular basis, i.e., daily, weekly or biweekly? If not, how can you change your lifestyle to include them more regularly? If yes, are they sufficient to substantially reduce your current stressors?"

7. Process by discussing what each group member would like to change (legitimately) in life to make it more pleasurable and less stressful.

Activity handout and facilitator's information adapted from submission by Corrie Trattner, M.S., OTR/L, Springfield, MA.

A Plan for Staying Alive!

What is depression? ____________________

TO GET READY to make a SURVIVAL plan, let's talk about your...

- thoughts of suicide
- feelings of suicide
- actions to consider when thinking and/or feeling suicidal

THE PLAN:

- ✔ WHO do I need to talk to when I'm feeling depressed? ____________________
- ✔ WHAT do I need when I'm feeling this way? ____________________
- ✔ WHERE do I go for help? ____________________
- ✔ WHEN do I need to tell someone that I am feeling suicidal? ____________________
- ✔ WHY do I need to say something and/or do something that tells people I need help? ____________________
- ✔ HOW will other people recognize my cues that indicate that I'm thinking about suicide if I am unable to ask for help? ____________________

The Agreement

When I feel ____________________

- *I promise I will tell you*
- *I promise I will ask for help*

Signature ____________________

Witness ____________________

When YOU feel ____________________

- *I promise I will listen*
- *I promise I will help you to get help*

Signature ____________________

Witness ____________________

SHAKE ON IT!

A Plan for Staying Alive!

I. PURPOSE:

To assist in developing a survival plan and contract.

II. GENERAL COMMENTS:

For many people with depression and suicidal feelings, the impulse to actually implement a suicide plan comes and goes as the ambivalence and uncertainty about life and death fluctuates. Developing a survival plan and a contract (the agreement) offers support and guidance in what is often a dark and confusing time, where choices are not clearly seen. An in-depth dialogue as provided in this activity is extremely helpful as an adjunct to a risk assessment scale.

III. POSSIBLE ACTIVITIES:

A. 1. Distribute the handouts asking group members to complete first question, "What is depression?" Discuss commonalities and differences.

2. Discuss next three subjects in the "To get ready . . . " section, highlighting individuals' ambivalence, e.g., "Part of you feels suicide is the only answer but part of you is still looking for another way."
3. Ask group members to complete "The Plan".
4. Encourage the prevention of self-harm and provide group members with an increased sense of control by engaging in a written partnership contract called "The Agreement", completing the top half of the agreement.
5. "Shake on it" with each group member.
6. Ask group member to find a partner to complete the "When you feel . . . " section of the agreement and ask partners to "shake on it".
7. Process by asking group members to summarize the session and to state the benefits.

B. 1. Distribute handouts.

2. Instruct group members to complete the left side of handout.
3. Divide group into pairs.
4. Encourage sharing of information. Offer the following suggestions to the listeners . . .

   stay calm
   encourage the person to talk
   listen
   express concern
   notice and mention strengths
5. Instruct partners to complete "The Agreement" together and to "shake on it".
6. Reconvene as a larger group and reinforce the meaning and strength of a contract.
7. Process by asking for volunteers to share written agreement.

Activity handout and facilitator's information adapted from submission by Sharen Bowen, R.P.N., Ottawa, ON.

Suicide Survivors

You got through the worst.

The worst has already happened!

Words can be powerful, especially when you're hurting, angry, sad and vulnerable. Choose the words that convey what you mean and that are consistent with your values as well as your beliefs about the person that you've lost. Decide on the term you're most comfortable saying:

S/he died suddenly.
S/he committed suicide.

S/he took his/her life.
S/he died.

S/he died by suicide.
S/he killed her/himself.

______________________ ______________________ ______________________

There seems to be a natural curiosity about suicide. People sometimes comment, question and give advice, which catches us off guard. It helps to have a "prepared" response. Write what you could say that's reasonably comfortable to you.

How many children / siblings do you have? (answer if loved one was child or sibling) ____________

How's ______________________? I haven't seen her/him for a while. ____________

Why did s/he do it? ______________________

How did s/he do it? ______________________

Who found him/her? ______________________

How did you find out? ______________________

Couldn't you have done something to help him/her? ______________________

Do you feel guilty? ______________________

Did you know s/he had problems / was sick? ______________________

Was s/he able to talk to you? ______________________

Did s/he go for help? ______________________

Was s/he on drugs? ______________________

You'll get over it soon. ______________________

You are so strong and are coping so well! ______________________

You'll never get over it. ______________________

How are you doing? ______________________

I'm sorry. ______________________

Are there other questions or comments that are particularly painful or difficult?

____

Are there questions or comments that are kind and comforting?

____

You will never be back to the old normal . . . Grief means building a new normal.

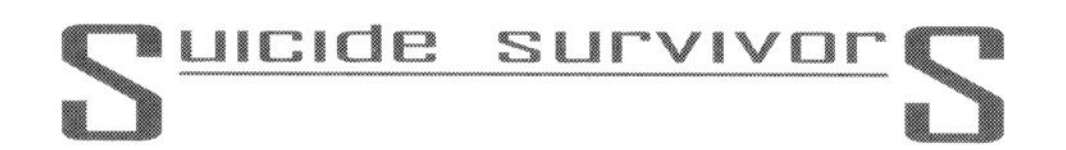

I. PURPOSE:

To assist the *suicide survivor* (any person grieving a suicide death) in the grieving process by becoming prepared for what might be uncomfortable conversations and questions.

II. GENERAL COMMENTS:

There are currently 30,000 suicides each year in the USA alone and about 3500 in Canada. About one million people worldwide take their own lives each year. These actual numbers may be higher, due to under-reporting. *Survivors of suicide* represent the largest mental health casualty area related to suicide. *Surviving family members* not only suffer the trauma of losing a loved one to suicide, but are themselves at higher risk for suicide and emotional problems. *Suicide survivors* are many times put apart from other *grieving* people. Assumptions are sometimes made that they have 'massive guilt' and were somehow in complicity with the death. They have to contend with people who avoid them, or people who talk about and/or are curious about the person who died. Death brings an end to one life, but is only the prelude to loss in other lives. The suffering of *survivors* is intense, complex and paradoxical, as the act of self-destruction itself. Suicide, unlike other deaths, is a deliberate severance from one's own self and life and from others who have been part of that life. Suicide is an untimely chosen death, carried out alone and most often secretly. The isolation, secrecy and disconnection of suicide becomes the survivor's legacy.

Generally it takes 18-24 months to stabilize after any death of a family member. At the time of the tragic event the survivor is in a state of shock or numbness. Four to seven months after the tragic event, the survivor usually is at a very low peak, and unfortunately, this may be the time when most people expect them to be "over the loss". Survivors need to talk about feelings, find appropriate ways to release bottled-up anger, take time to lament, feel sorry for themselves, cry, question and be weak. Being prepared to engage in conversations more comfortably allows the survivor to begin the healing process.

Parts of this handout are based on information from Suicide Survivors - A Guide for Those Left Behind by Adina Wrobleski.

III. POSSIBLE ACTIVITIES:

A. 1. Distribute handouts to suicide survivors.
   2. Ask each group member to complete the handout to the best of their ability, leaving questions blank that they feel unable or unwilling to answer.
   3. Discuss phrase "commit suicide" and how each group member feels about using that term in his/her particular situation. Emphasize that this is a very personal feeling, and seldom do people agree, even if from the same family.
   4. Asking for volunteers, elicit phrase with which each survivor feels most comfortable, and if able, why.
   5. Write the bottom line from the handout on a dry erase board. ("You will never be back to the old normal . . . Grief means building a new normal.")
   6. Discuss as a group the meaning of that sentence.
   7. Process benefit of activity discussing if, and how, each group member feels better prepared to respond to other people.

B. 1. Distribute handouts to suicide survivors.
   2. Ask each group member to complete the handout to the best of his/her ability, leaving questions blank that each one feels unable to answer.
   3. Discuss phrase "commit suicide" and how group members feel about using that term in their particular situation. Emphasize that this is a very personal feeling, and seldom do people agree, even if they're from the same family.
   4. Take a vote of responses to the term survivor's felt most comfortable with, asking for input if anyone has strong feeling about any of the terms.
   5. Lead a discussion using above stated PURPOSE and GENERAL COMMENTS. Ask group members to share responses to questions.
   6. Process activity by discussing the awareness that talking about the death, and feeling unprepared, seems to be a universal problem of most survivors.

HOW IS YOUR SPIRITUAL HEALTH?

Many people have beliefs that significantly affect their ways of life, their modes of dress, the foods they eat and their general values system. These beliefs often include spirituality, but frequently are overlooked due to a more physical or mental focus in life. A balance of mind, body and spirit can facilitate health. *Mind* is defined as mental activity, and *body* refers to physical being.

Spirituality encompasses purpose in life, relationships with others and/or a higher being, the need for hope, personal transcendence, communication and grief.

Indicate your life's balance of mind (M), body (B) and spirit (S) in the circle below.

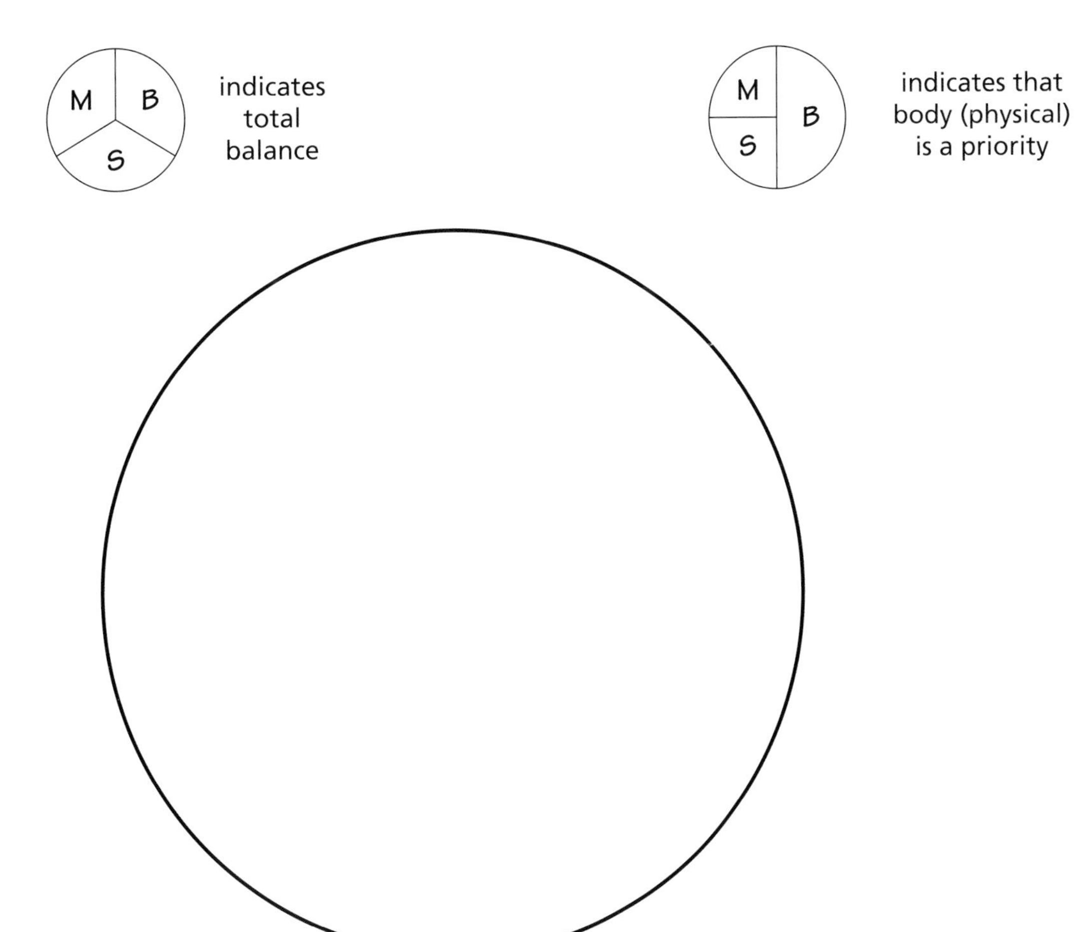

Divide *your* circle to indicate your balance of mind, body and spirit.
Next, write the activities inside each section that *you* do, that support these areas.

HOW IS YOUR SPIRITUAL HEALTH?

I. PURPOSE:

To discuss spiritual health in a comfortable, non-judgmental format.
To provide support for spiritual health.

II. GENERAL COMMENTS:

Many people have beliefs that significantly affect their ways of life, their modes of dress, the foods they eat and their general values systems. These beliefs often include spirituality, but frequently are overlooked due to a more physical or mental focus in life. A balance of mind, body and spirit can facilitate health. Mind is defined as mental activity, and body refers to physical being.

When discussing spiritual health, carefully consider how specific words might be interpreted differently based on peoples' past, cultural experiences and religious backgrounds. For example, the word "soul" might be interpreted in many ways. Also, use sensitivity as there might be words that *turn people off* and prevent positive facilitation of the intended topic.

III. POSSIBLE ACTIVITIES:

A. 1. Distribute handouts and discuss.

2. Present the following questions verbally or in written form, to stimulate discussion. These questions were chosen to be used with people who do not readily identify with their spiritual nature, but may be adapted easily to reflect spirituality as needed.
   - What holidays are important to you, if any?
   - Do you feel happier during certain times of the year? If so, when?
   - How do you spend a typical Saturday or Sunday?
   - Do you have a "lucky" color, number or phrase. *(Red is good luck for the Chinese people, the number 18 is "lucky" for the Jewish people, etc.)*
   - List all the milestones in your life that have significance to you.
   - What activities enhance your soul?
   - Do you have a favorite book? If so, what is it? Are there any books that you have read more than once? Why?
   - Who do you turn to when you need help?
   - Describe your ideal day.
   - Describe your ideal evening.
   - What type of music do you enjoy?

3. Using any modality, ask each group member to design a project that represents them. The outer layer is that which people see in them. The inner layer is what represents their soul (use the "soul" only if you think they'll be receptive to that word), their secrets, their fears, their hopes, etc. (This layer will be kept for themselves and is not to be shared.) *For example: Decorate a shoe box on the outside with things that represent the outer being (pictures of what one likes to do) and the inside with things that represent the inner being (cut out words which describe hopes, spirit, etc.)*

4. Discuss and share as a group the "outers" and stress the importance to have "inners" and know what they are.

B. 1. Distribute handouts and discuss.

2. Ask group members to draw a time-line on the reverse side of the handout, marking all the significant milestones in their lives.

3. Discuss what influence spirituality has had on them throughout their life span. Ask group members if their spirituality has changed or evolved throughout their lives.

4. Support group members by discussing that as our mind and body age and mature, so does our spiritual health.

5. Process by asking group members to identify ideas and goals on how to improve spiritual health.

Activity handout and facilitator's information adapted from submission by
Sandra Barker Dunbar, MA, OTR, Cooper City, FL and Natalie Gorlin, OTR, Salt Lake City, UT.

LIFE ASSESSMENT CHART

**USING THE FOLLOWING SCALE,
RATE IMPORTANCE OF THESE ITEMS TO YOU:**

1 - not important 2 - rarely important 3 - fairly important 4 - important 5 - very important

VALUES	1	2	3	4	5
✷ having a support system					
✷ being needed					
✷ feeling secure					
✷ outdoor activities					
✷ music					
✷ life balance					
✷ rituals					
✷ diversity in life					
✷ family gatherings					
✷ friends					
✷ religion					
✷ work					
✷ play					
✷ organization / structure					
✷ personal space					
✷ possessions					
✷ education					
✷ learning					
✷ milestones					
✷ achievement					
✷ goals					
✷ money					
✷ death					
✷ intimacy / sex					

LIFE ASSESSMENT CHART

I. PURPOSE:

To identify values that represent the focus of a person's life.

II. GENERAL COMMENTS:

It is valuable to discover what areas of life are important to us and why. Our lives should focus on the themes of high value to each of us. It is important to evaluate if these answers indicate a spiritual, mental or physical focus.

III. POSSIBLE ACTIVITIES:

A. 1. Distribute handouts, instructing group members to complete.

2. Use the LIFE ASSESSMENT CHART to help group members discover areas that represent values. Discuss in a group setting whether answers are in the mental, physical or spiritual realm.

3. Encourage group members to discuss why certain items were valued more than others by giving examples, i.e., If music was rated as very important, describe what type of music is enjoyed.

4. Process by asking group members to identify which values they considered to be their greatest strengths in their everyday lives.

B 1. Distribute handout to group members.

2. Ask each group member to consider his/her life history in one, two or three chapters; a main event can be divided into time periods, for example:

   childhood, adulthood
   first job, second job
   moving to 3 different locations
   college, marriage, parenthood

3. Identify which values were most important in which chapter. (This can be graded by choosing just two or three values.)

4. Process by discussing why certain values were chosen and whether this activity will influence their values and choices in the future.

Activity handout and facilitator's information adapted from submission by
Natalie Gorlin, OTR, Salt Lake City, UT and Sandra Barker Dunbar, MA, OTR, Cooper City, FL.

GROOMING & HYGIENE CHECKLIST

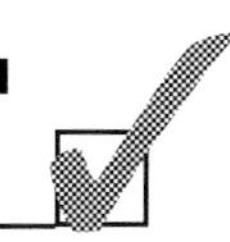

	SUN	MON	TUES	WED	THUR	FRI	SAT
Bath or shower							
Shampoo hair							
Comb hair							
Brush teeth							
Clean face and hands							
Apply deodorant							
Clean & trim nails							
Clothing neat & clean							
Use of powder / lotion							
Use aftershave / makeup							
OVERALL APPEARANCE: rate 1-10 (10 best)							

COMMENTS: ____

____

____

____

____

PURPOSE:

To provide an organizational tool that will assist in developing and maintaining adequate grooming and hygiene.

Supplemental activity handout adapted from submission by Laura M. Grogan, OTR/L, Washington, D.C.
in collaboration with Susan F. Miller, OTR/L, Washington, D.C.

Healing Meditation

As I go into my inner self for guidance with healing, I am transcending the everyday flow of information. When this happens, I know I am going to a place where the outside world has no meaning and I am safe. This is a space that is mine alone -- it is my security, my oasis, my respite from troubles and from illness and pain. When I am here I know a peace so deep, so satisfying, that I relax completely, breathing in only pure air and breathing out all the waste from the stress I have built up over the days and months and years. Deep stress, deeply ingrained, now being released more and more with each out-breath.

Now as I go deeper, all my muscles are relaxing, and I am breathing healing white light into each wounded or painful or disabled or tired area each time I breathe.

My inner journey takes me into the deepest inner recesses of my being now, a place of only light and a loving, enveloping stillness that cushions my body and mind. All cares drift away into the void and are gone for now. Only the marshmallow softness of my inner being surrounds me, and allows my thinking processes to slow and to gravitate naturally to their source, which is Oneness; the Divine spark within me. From here all creativity springs, from here all healing occurs. As one reaches out into the manifest world to accomplish its work, the other works in tandem.

I am aware, as I sit here, quietly, serenely attuned to the inner dance of wisdom that is my true Self, that I can heal my life with my creative processes just as I can create injury, illness, frustration, anxiety and unhappiness in my life. All I need do is to create a more accepting, loving, forgiving approach to these so-called "problems". The healing I seek has always been right here, within me - I need DO nothing to attain it. I need not "change" myself outwardly - I need not adopt new behaviors or a new job or a new mate or a new physique.

All I need do is accept the light that is within me, waiting, always waiting, to be perceived and acknowledged. Then, as I begin to accept the light within me - the light that I am, I can begin to allow it to shine on the areas of my body and of my life that need to be healed. All I need do is love myself a little more on a daily basis to allow this beautiful, nurturing light to shine on the darkest inner recesses of my psyche, where I thought nothing could ever reach.

I do not even like to acknowledge its existence, for I rejected that part of myself long ago - long ago as a small child when I learned that this part of me was not acceptable. My pain from that experience told me to turn away from that unacceptable part of myself, and over the years I lost touch with it until one day I must have stopped feeling anything in that area altogether. It became a lost child of its own, abandoned by me in my pain and inability to understand that I need not reject any part of myself to please others. If I cried over that lost child, I did not know its name, for its identity has changed over the years. I only know that now I have pain of another kind, from the betrayal of myself, my own flesh, and this pain is so much worse now, as an adult, precisely because I do not know its name.

I feel it is a part of me, and yet do not know where to begin to heal it. Sometimes it is physical pain, sometimes a longing for more, or a deep feeling that something is missing, something I had long ago that could make me whole now. And I don't know where to begin to look.

I want to welcome my rejected child, wherever it is, that betrayed, pained part of my self, back into my heart now. I know now that I must own all my feelings, all my behaviors, all my beliefs and opinions to be truly who I was meant to be. And being who I am is what I was sent here to do. That is all that was ever expected of me. To be who I am.

So I allow myself now, in this safe, secure space deep within my inner self, to remember that original pain as it was when I first experienced it, and to allow it to feel welcomed by the love I now have in my heart for it. I know I could not handle it well as a child, and I forgive myself for stuffing it away in the dark where it could not be seen.

I know I did the best I could at the time. Now I can see it for what it really is - a beloved part of my greater self and as such, a part of my higher purpose for being here on Earth. There is no shame, no guilt connected to it as I had mistakenly thought. It is a beautiful, soulful part of my Self that asks only to be welcomed home.

~

Welcome this lost child back into your heart now. Welcome him back, for he has wandered long and lonely in the wilderness and had almost given up hope of being rescued. Speak softly to him your words of acceptance and forgiveness and love, for he is your own. He will respond with love of his own if you can do this, and that love will take the form of healing in your life.

In whatever form it is needed, that healing will begin to take place as soon as you welcome him home and remember to keep him in your heart. He will need more attention than your other children, for he has been alone in his sadness for so long. As you lavish your loving attention on him, he will bring you the healing you seek, and then you will realize that it is you who have created the healing from the Source of your Being. You can create that now --- with love.

Healing Meditation

PURPOSE:

To provide a meditation script in healing.

Supplemental activity handout submitted by Diane Hausler, LSW, Fairview Park, OH.

Meditation on "Letting Go" of Control

I know, when I look at my life, that I have tried to control too many situations so they will turn out the way I think is best. And I know now, that so often when I have done this, I end up unhappy, frustrated and unfulfilled, not knowing why at the time. This is a pattern I have followed all my life. One that doesn't really seem to be working for me now that I am aware of how fruitless it is to attempt to control things that just can't BE controlled.

I didn't know that by "letting go" and having more faith -- that things would always turn out for the best -- that I would free myself of my never-ending cycle of control, frustration and disappointment. I didn't realize that it is not always possible for me to know how things should go in order for the greater good to occur. And I didn't know that by having a little patience, I would be demonstrating faith in the Divine plan.

If I have shown less than faith in something greater than myself throughout my life, I know better now, and I want to begin to live the faith I have always heard about and even thought I had but didn't really.

I know that letting go of my need to judge and control things in my life is a process, and I don't expect to be able to do it well overnight. But it does represent a new way of seeing how life can work when you believe that you do not always know what the best outcome will be. I make the commitment now to begin to find my way down that path of trust in a wisdom greater than my own could ever be.

I can begin now to see everything in my life with new eyes - to see every situation I encounter as a lesson and every person I encounter as a teacher. In this way I will open my eyes to a more loving, positive and exciting way of living; one that is infused with the wonder of NOT KNOWING. Because that is where the true mystery of life is, and it requires my willingness to just let it be a mystery.

I know that as I continue to see my life as a series of lessons, I will feel less and less need to set an agenda of my own, and instead can begin to step aside a little, in order to allow my life to unfold naturally. I am ready to begin to trust in this process, and I know it is a way which will bring miracles into my life in the form of a deeper understanding of who I really am, why I am here, and how interconnected I am with all living beings.

I am ready now to be open to all new situations, to not fight against anything just because I am afraid it might be a bad or negative or painful experience. I am willing to be open to the possibility that my greatest joy may lie waiting for me just around the corner, and it may be disguised in one such seemingly negative experience.

I am open now to the possibility, at least, that this is so, and that I may not really be in a position to judge such things. I open my mind and my heart to the spirit within me and around me that does, sometimes mysteriously, always know what is ultimately the best for me.

I acknowledge that I may sometimes only see how necessary a situation was for my happiness and personal growth after it has occurred. That I may need to experience what at the time feels painful or difficult or against my own judgment in order to learn the lesson that only later will I recognize as a loving, spiritual step in the direction of greater joy and self-realization for me in this life.

And I know that as these life lessons unfold more and more naturally for me because I allow them to, I will begin to accept myself, my life, and others in a more profound way, and I will have so much more richness in my life to share that I will begin to actually seek out experiences which before I might have avoided.

I understand that life is no more and no less than a series of lessons, and I play the role of student who is here only to learn and then pass that learning along to others in a gentle, non-judgmental way. And that the purpose underlying all the lessons I seem to be learning is just this: to grow in wisdom and to learn to love myself and others better.

That is all that was ever expected of me.

That is why I am here.

Meditation on "Letting Go" of Control

PURPOSE:

To provide a meditation script to assist in "letting go" of control.

Supplemental activity handout submitted by Diane Hausler, LSW, Fairview Park, OH.

PEOPLE WITH MENTAL ILLNESS ENRICH OUR LIVES

Abraham Lincoln

1809-1865. The sixteenth president of the United States, known for his "invariable fairness and utter honesty", in addition to his great strides in civil rights. He received about the equivalent of one year of formal education when he decided to learn on his own. He taught himself law and became one of the most successful and recognized attorneys of his day. Mr. Lincoln fell into "terrible depression and despondency" over his broken engagement to Mary Todd. His mother's death in 1818 also had the same effect on him. –*Encyclopedia Brittanica*, vol. 23, pp. 42-48. Lincoln suffered from depression. –*Abraham Lincoln* 6 volumes written by Carl Sandburg.

Beethoven

1770-1827. "A universal genius widely regarded as the greatest composer who ever lived." Major works include: The Five Piano Concertos and Symphonies 1 through 9. He believed in "the power of music to convey a philosophy of life without the aid of a spoken text". His personal life was marked by his desperate struggle to fight off his encroaching deafness. Losing the battle, he became withdrawn.–*Encyclopedia Brittanica*, vol. 27, pp. 219-220. "Like many of his appreciators, this man suffered from the disease of dual personality. –*Beethoven* by Schauffler.

Patty Duke

1946- . An Oscar and Emmy winning actress. "As with many people, the overt symptoms of my manic-depressive illness didn't show themselves until my late teens. And that was with a manic episode. From that time on, until I was diagnosed at the age of thirty-five, I rode a wild rollercoaster, from agitated, out-of-control highs to disabling, often suicidal lows." –*A Brilliant Madness* by Patty Duke and Gloria Hochman.

Robert Schumann

1810-1856. A German composer who was best known for his romantic piano music, songs and orchestral music. He also possessed an inclination for writing plays and poems. He suffered despair over his broken engagement to Clara Wieck. In 1844, he "suffered a serious nervous collapse". He was in recovery until 1850. In 1845, during his recovery he spent 10 months writing a symphony. In February of 1854, he "complained of a very strong and painful attack of the ear malady that had troubled him before; this was followed by aural illusions; such as the dictation by angels of a theme on which he proceeded to write some variations for piano". Two weeks later he "asked to be taken to a lunatic asylum and the next day attempted suicide by drowning. He had contemplated suicide on at least three occasions during the '30's". Two weeks later, he was "removed to a private asylum . . . where he lived for nearly two and a half years until his death". –*Encyclopedia Brittanica*, vol. 10, pp. 543-546. He suffered from psychotic depression. –*"Bipolar Affective Disorder and Creativity: Implications and Clinical Management"* by Nancy Andreason and Ira Glick in *Comprehensive Psychiatry*, May / June 1988.

LEO TOLSTOY

1828-1910. Russian author, reformer and moral thinker credited with writing what is considered the best piece of literature of all time, *War and Peace*. Tolstoy lived a happy life in his marriage and as a novelist, "until his incessant probing into the meaning of life drove him to a 'spiritual crisis'. In 1879 he contemplated suicide." Those who knew him well spoke of his "duality of character", seeing him as a "deeply contradictory man". –*Encyclopedia Brittanica*, vol. 28, pp. 707-711. "We may mention Tolstoy's conversion following upon a mid-life crisis at the age of fifty in which he became pathologically depressed." –*Dynamics of Creation* by Anthony Storr.

John Keats

1795-1821. An English poet of the Romantic Period. He was concerned with the joy in this world and sorrow in passing on. His work attempts to bridge that gap with understanding. ". . . since he not only alleges that he has "no self" and no identical nature, but that the identities of others annihilate him – a complaint familiar to psychiatrists, since schizoid people constantly echo it." " 'Oh! What misery it is to have an intellect in splints!' " –*Dynamics of Creation* by Anthony Storr.

Edgar Allan Poe

1809-1849. An American poet, critic, and writer of short stories. He was known for his development of mystery and the macábre in fiction writing as evidenced in *The Raven*. "Drinking was . . . to be the bane of his life." According to medical testimony he had a "brain lesion". "The outstanding fact in Poe's character is a strange duality. The wide divergence of contemporary judgements on the man seems almost to point to the co-existence of two persons in him."–*Encyclopedia Brittanica*, vol 9, pp. 540-541.

Isaac Newton

1643-1727. An English physicist and mathematician best known for his advances in: laws of motion, universal gravitation, science of light, infinitesimal calculus, and physical optics. He had an, "acute sense of insecurity that rendered him obsessively anxious when his work was published and irrationally violent when he defended it [which] accompanied [him] throughout his life and can plausibly be traced to his early years". "For nine years, Isaac was separated from his mother, and his pronounced psychotic tendencies have been ascribed to this traumatic event [which he blamed directly on his stepfather]." When his dearest friend became ill, Newton suffered what was believed to have been at least his second nervous breakdown. He eventually recovered his stability, but ceased his scientific efforts. –*Encyclopedia Brittanica*, vol. 24, pp. 892-895. He suffered from psychotic depression. –*"Bipolar Affective Disorder and Creativity: Implications and Clinical Management"* by Nancy Andreason and Ira Glick in *Comprehensive Psychiatry*, May / June 1988.

Michelangelo

1475-1564. Michelangelo Buonarroti is regarded as one of the greatest sculptors of all time. He has received unequalled recognition during the Renaissance for his paintings, architecture, and drawings. He has been credited by some for the existence of the Renaissance, Reformation and Baroque Periods. –*Encyclopedia Brittanica*, vol. 24, pp. 55-59. "Yet this universally recognized genius... remained, as his sonnets demonstrate, forever the prey of depression and self-denigration." –*The Dynamics of Creation* by Anthony Storr.

Charles Dickens

1812-1870. Generally regarded as the greatest English novelist. Dickens had received greater recognition than any author had received in his / her lifetime. Major works: *David Copperfield, Oliver Twist, Great Expectations, Pickwick Papers,* and *A Christmas Carol*. In 1855, Dickens sunk into personal unhappiness after living a very happy public and private life. –*Encyclopedia Brittanica*, vol. 17, pp. 267-272. "But of course he was not always in such control of himself. 'He had strange fits of depression from time to time', says Henry Felding Dickens." –*The Man Charles Dickens* by Edward Wagenkencht, 1929. "George Elliot and Charles Dickens began their novels in states of depression that lifted as the books progressed. Dickens became manic upon finishing his books but Elliot apparently did not." –*The Key to Genius: Manic Depression and the Creative Life*, p. 34, by D. Jablow Hershman and Julia Lieb, MD; Promestheus Books, 1988.

PEOPLE WITH MENTAL ILLNESS ENRICH OUR LIVES

PURPOSE:

To provide biographical data about famous people that enriched our lives, who have/had serious mental illnesses. Refer to PEOPLE WITH MENTAL ILLNESS ENRICH OUR LIVES (page 4), for activity handout.

STEPPING UP TO YOUR GOALS!

Goals sometimes seem so far away and hard to reach.
The skill of breaking them down into little steps helps us to reach them.

STEPPING UP TO YOUR GOALS!

PURPOSE:

To provide a method of achieving a seemingly overwhelming goal by breaking it down into small, attainable steps.

EXAMPLE:

1st STEP: I'm going to reorganize and clean my "junk" drawer by Friday.

2nd STEP: I'll tell my neighbor about it.

3rd STEP:
- a) I'm going to take everything out of the drawer and put it all in a box.
- b) Then I'll clean the drawer.
- c) I'll then make selections.
- d) Next, I'll throw out what I don't need.
- e) Finally, I'll put everything back into its own organized place.

4th STEP: I'm going to spend some time with my neighbor, doing something special.

The Stress Management Contract

Today's date ______________________________

I, ______________________________ *promise that when I feel stressed,*
(name)

I WILL . . .

1) ____

____.

2) ____

____.

3) ____

____.

4) ____

____.

*I also promise to place this contract somewhere that I can see it **daily** to remind me to use positive coping skills.*

Signed ____

Witnessed by ____

The Stress Management Contract

PURPOSE:

To provide a formal agreement facilitating the implementation of positive coping skills.

Activity handout and facilitator's information adapted from submission by Pamela A. Joy, COTA/L, Canton, OH.

Stress Management Game

Describe stress.	Describe a relaxation technique.
State 2 POSITIVE ways to deal with stress.	State 2 NEGATIVE ways to deal with stress.
Describe a positive way to relax.	Why do we work on "stress management"?
What can happen to our body when we're under stress?	Do we need STRESS in our lives?
Why is relaxation so important?	Name one way to let your feelings out (vent) when you are stressed.
What is a stress symptom, or a warning sign?	What is distress or "bad" stress?
True or false? Caffeine or "junk food" help us when we feel stressed. Why or why not?	True or false? Bad habits develop when we use negative ways to cope with stress over and over again. Explain your answer.
What is a good stressor?	True or false? Exercise can help to relieve stress. Why or why not?
Can leisure ("fun") activities help to relieve stress? Why or why not?	True or false? There's nothing you can do about stress. Explain your answer.
Describe how you feel physically when you are stressed.	Describe how you feel emotionally when you are stressed.

The $1,000 StResS MANAGEMENT Game

PURPOSE:

To provide a fun format for learning about stress management and its basic concepts.

INSTRUCTIONS:

1. Copy handout and cut along dotted lines.
2. Place questions face down in one stack.
3. Divide the group into two teams, asking one person to keep score.
4. One team member, from team #1 picks a card and can discuss the questions with his/her team members for one minute.
5. Team member who chose the card then reads the card aloud, and answers it as thoroughly as possible, representing the group.
6. If the answer is acceptable, the team wins 150 points (or $150 in WELLNESS BUCKS from the supplemental page 59 in Life Management Skills III). Give less points or bucks for incomplete answers.
7. Team #2 repeats steps four, five and six.
8. The first team that acquires $1,000 in WELLNESS BUCKS or 1,000 points, wins the game.
9. Prizes can be awarded to winning team or they can choose the next activity, gain extra privileges, etc.

Supplemental activity handout and instructions adapted from submission by Pamela A. Joy, COTA/L, Canton, OH.

WELLNESS CONTRACT

I,____

(name)

hereby commit myself to making good on the goals I have selected.

THESE GOALS ARE:

GOAL 1:____________________________________

____

GOAL 2:____________________________________

____

GOAL 3:____________________________________

____

To witness that I have made this commitment, I have asked the following friends to sign my contract. They know I'm really serious about this.

____

Signature

____________________ ____________________

First witness: Second witness:

Wellness Contract

PURPOSE:

To provide an opportunity to improve the prospect of succeeding and planning for wellness.

Supplemental activity handout from Donald B. Ardell, Ph.D.,
Ardell Wellness Report, 9901 Lake Georgia Drive, Orlando, FL 32817.

'WHO' ICE BREAKERS

WHO PLAYS A SPORT?

WHO CAN DO A CARTWHEEL?

WHOSE FAVORITE COLOR IS ORANGE?

WHO HAS EVER RECEIVED AN AWARD?

WHO WAS BORN ON A HOLIDAY?

WHO HAS A FAVORITE TV PROGRAM THAT IS ON THURSDAY NIGHT? NAME IT.

WHO IS NAMED AFTER A FAMILY MEMBER?

WHO IS WEARING ANY TYPE OF JEWELRY THAT REFLECTS HIS/HER NAME?

WHO CAN NAME THE FIRST AMERICAN ASTRONAUT THAT WALKED ON THE MOON?

WHO HAS RECENTLY READ A BOOK? NAME THAT BOOK.

WHO PLAYS AN INSTRUMENT? WHAT IS IT?

WHO SPEAKS ANOTHER LANGUAGE?

WHO HAS A FIRST NAME THAT BEGINS WITH THE LETTER "T"?

WHO HAS AN UNUSUAL PET? WHAT IS IT?

WHO IS WEARING THE COLOR PURPLE?

WHO HAS TRAVELED TO ANOTHER COUNTRY? WHICH COUNTRY?

WHO LIKES TO EAT COOKED SPINACH?

WHO RECENTLY SAW A MOVIE IN THE THEATER? NAME THE MOVIE.

'WHO' ICE BREAKERS

PURPOSE:

To provide a fun, non-threatening way to warm-up a group for an activity.

Supplemental activity handout adapted from submission by Michele Vitelli, Motivational Instructor, Skippack, PA.

ORDER FORM

First Name | Last Name | MI
Title | Department
Facility
Address (cannot deliver to a P.O. Box)
City | State | Zip + four
Phone | Fax

Home Address
City | State | Zip + four
Home Phone | Country
E-mail Address

Order Code	Quantity	Name of Product / Description	Language or Size (if applicable)	Price Each	Total Price
B—LM1		LIFE MANAGEMENT SKILLS I		$ 37.95	
B—LM2		LIFE MANAGEMENT SKILLS II		$ 37.95	
B—LM3		LIFE MANAGEMENT SKILLS III		$ 39.95	
B—LM4		LIFE MANAGEMENT SKILLS IV		$ 39.95	
K—LC4		KIT - LIFE MANAGEMENT SKILLS IV book and cards (value $54.90)		$ 49.95	
K—LM4		KIT - LIFE MANAGEMENT SKILLS I, II, III, IV (value $155.80)		$ 139.95	
K—LS4		KIT - LMS I, II, III, IV and 4 decks of corresponding cards (value $215.60)		$ 193.95	
K—PP4		KIT - LMS I, II, III, IV, 4 decks of cards, BSC game, EMOTIONS© poster (value $270.55)		$ 246.95	
P—AFF		POSITIVE AFFIRMATIONS laminated poster 24"x36" (page 36)		$ 14.95	
P—IAM		I AM SOMEONE WHO laminated poster 24"x36" (page 35)		$ 14.95	
P—LEI		LEISURE SCAVENGER HUNT laminated poster 24"x36" (page 23)		$ 14.95	
P—STP		STEPPING UP TO YOUR GOALS laminated poster 24"x36" (page 55)		$ 14.95	
OTHER					
OTHER					
OTHER					
OTHER					
OTHER					

Method of Payment:

- ☐ Check or money order in U.S. funds payable to Wellness Reproductions Inc.
- ☐ Purchase Order (must be attached)
- ☐ Visa ☐ MasterCard
- ☐ Discover ☐ American Express

Account Number | Expiration Date

Signature ______________________

SUBTOTAL

Ohio orders – add 7% sales tax or tax ID #

✻ SHIPPING/HANDLING – SEE BELOW

GRAND TOTAL (U.S. funds only)

Three Easy Ways to Order:

To expedite all orders, please include suite number.

1.

Call Us Toll-Free:

1/800/669-9208
Monday-Friday
7:30 AM to 4:30 PM E.S.T.

2.

Send Us:

Wellness Reproductions Inc.
23945 Mercantile Road
Suite B47
Beachwood, OH 44122-5924

3.

Fax Us:

1/216/831-1355
24 hours a day
7 days a week

The Wellness Guarantee

Wellness Reproductions Inc. stands behind it's products 100%. We will refund, exchange or credit your account for the price of any materials returned within 30 days of receipt. Materials must be in resalable condition. Simply return the item with the packing slip and reason to: Wellness Reproductions Inc. 23945 Mercantile Road Beachwood, Ohio 44122-5924

✻ Shipping/Handling Charges

Continental USA

- Minimum $3.75
- Under $250 .... add 10%
- Over $250.......... add 8%
- Over $500.......... add 6%

Rush Delivery
Call for additional charge.
In-stock items will be shipped the next business day and arrive within two more business days.

Overnight Delivery
Call for additional charge.
In-stock items ordered by noon will arrive the following business day.

CANADA
Call Sunnyside Book Shop at 1/613-241-0943 or fax at 1/613-241-4422.

Outside of Continental USA
AK, HI, and Canada add an additional $10.00 to shipping/handling charges above. Other foreign countries call for shipping/handling charges.
Puerto Rico and all foreign countries, prepay U.S. Funds only or use credit card.
Shipments outside of the United States are subject to additional handling charges and fees. Customers are responsible for any applicable taxes and duties.

Our Order Policies ensure fast, efficient service!

SALES TAX: Ohio residents add 7% sales tax on total. Tax-exempt organizations, please provide exempt or resale number when ordering.

MAILING: Every order, including small orders, will receive our best service. However, a minimum charge of $3.75 handling and mailing must be added to offset the cost of processing the order. Deliveries are sent within 48 hours of receipt unless notified otherwise. Continental US orders are shipped UPS ground. Please provide complete street address. UPS cannot deliver to a post office box. Please allow 7 working days for delivery. We can ship UPS COD and an additional $6.00 will be added to your order.

TERMS: Purchase orders, net 30 days. International orders must be prepaid in U.S. Funds.

PRICING: Prices effective February 1997. This order form supersedes all previous brochures. Prices subject to change without notice. If this form has expired, we will bill you any difference in price.

UNIVERSITY INSTRUCTOR? If you are considering using any of our materials as a school text or supplemental resource, please call our office to discuss desk copies and quantity education discounts.

METHODS OF PAYMENT: To expedite ALL orders, please include suite number listed after our address on your order form. **Check:** Make payable to Wellness Reproductions Inc. **Purchase Order:** Mail or fax a purchase order. Be sure to include name of person using products, title, and department. **Credit Card:** Please include account number, expiration date and signature. **Don't forget the Suite #!**

UPDATE OUR MAILING LIST: You are automatically added to our permanent mailing list when you order your first product from us. If you want to change your address, remove your name, or eliminate duplicate names from our file, please write to us. Until we correct our duplicate mailing, please pass along an extra copy of this catalogue to one of your colleagues.

PROBLEMS? WE'LL TAKE CARE OF THEM! If anything we send is damaged or lost in shipping, or if anything is mistakenly left out of your order–we will take care of it immediately. All you need to do is note any damages on the packing slip and ship back in the original shipping carton and packing material within 10 days. We'll take care of the rest! Call us if there was a shortage and we will send it to you.

Please photocopy, complete and mail to Wellness Reproductions Inc., 23945 Mercantile Road, Beachwood, OH 44122-5924

If you fill out items 1, 2, 3 & 4 on this feedback page, you can return it with the order form on the other side and take **10%** off of the subtotal.

FEEDBACK - LIFE MANAGEMENT SKILLS IV

1. Check the topics that were of special interest to you in LMS IV.

____ Activities of Daily Living	____ Job Readiness	____ Self-Esteem
____ Combatting Stigma	____ Journalizing	____ Sexual Health
____ Communication	____ Leisure	____ Social Skills
____ Coping With Serious Mental Illness	____ Parenting	____ Stress Management
____ Home Management	____ Relationships	____ Suicide Issues
____ Humor	____ Responsibility	____ Values

2. What topics would be of interest in future publications?
   a) ____________________
   b) ____________________
   c) ____________________

3. Which were your favorite handouts?
   a) ____________________
   b) ____________________
   c) ____________________

4. Describe an activity that you have created for any of the pages in this book.

____

____

____

If this activity can be published in our WELLNESS NET•WORK newsletter, please sign with your professional initials for publication. If it is selected, you will receive a presentation poster of your choice.

(signature) ____________________

5. Comments on LMS IV: ____________________

____

____

Can these comments be published? ______ Yes ______ No

(signature) ____________________ *(date)* ____________________

Name ____________________ Title ____________________

Facility ____________________ Occupation ____________________

Address ____________________ Home Address ____________________

City ____________________ City ____________________

State ____________ Zip ________ State ____________ Zip ________

Phone (work) (   ) ____________ Phone (home) (   ) ____________

(SEE REVERSE SIDE FOR ORDER FORM)